A YEAR IN THE FIELDS | THE STATE OF THE WASHINGTON FARMER

THE SPOKESMAN-REVIEW

FOREWORD

By Rob Curley, Editor

THE SPOKESMAN-REVIEW

Like all places, there's typically a big difference between how the locals view their communities and how the rest of the world views them. It was that very idea that set up one of The Spokesman-Review's most in-depth series in our newspaper's 135-year-history: "A Year in the Fields."

Long before Boeing, Microsoft, Starbucks or Amazon, Washington was known for its world-class agriculture. Apple orchards and waving wheatfields. Hops for the finest beers and potatoes perfect for your favorite french fries.

Most of the world now sees our state very differently — the home of high-tech, high-flying jets and highly caffeinated beverages. Yet, agriculture still is very much at the heart of what makes Washington what it is.

Our soil, weather and irrigation allows farmers and orchardists to grow many types of crops, from blueberries, onions and tulips, to asparagus, oysters and wine grapes. The diversity makes Washington one of our nation's most important farming states.

But what is the health of the Washington farm and farmer?

Finding that answer would be the point of our entire series.

When we first started planning for it in the winter of 2017, a year seemed like plenty of time to try to learn as much as we could about the state of the Washington farmer and tell our readers all about it. It wasn't.

The series formally ran in our paper's pages from April of 2017 until this fall. Even now, we're not exactly sure we're done telling these stories.

The changing technology. The politics and trade. The actual farms worked by real families. Along with fears and uncertainties, we also found hope, courage and pride.

Back when I was a young reporter, I was told one of our biggest responsibilities as journalists was to give a voice to the voiceless.

We wanted to show the world that Washington was much more than just Amazon and Starbucks. We wanted to give our state's farmers the voice they deserved.

We accomplished that and much more.

Our agricultural series has become a mirror for readers, who were reminded of the perseverance, hard work and risk required to operate a modern farm. And who delighted in their own memories or those of their parents and grandparents who started their lives in farm country.

This level of commitment was not unusual for this newspaper. The Spokesman-Review has long been there for the Washington farmer. Editions in the early 1900s even carried the tagline "The Farmer's Family Newspaper" at the top of our front page.

We will continue to be a powerful voice for the Washington farmer for our next 135 years.

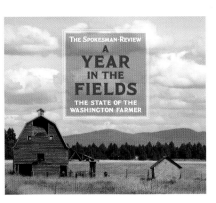

OPPOSITE: Dani Monroe, the 2017 Queen of Cashmere, rides an apple blossom float in Wenatchee's Stemilt Growers Grand Parade during the 2017 Apple Blossom Festival in Wenatchee, Wash. TYLER TJOMSLAND / THE SPOKESMAN-REVIEW

ON THE COVER: The old barn in a field — this one just north of Spokane — remains a lasting symbol of the family farm in Washington.
TYLER TJOMSLAND / THE SPOKESMAN-REVIEW

Published by Pediment Publishing, a division of The Pediment Group, Inc.
www.pediment.com
Printed in the United States of America.

CONTENTS

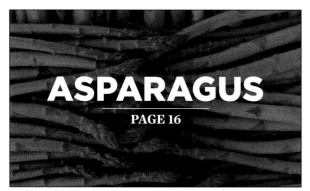

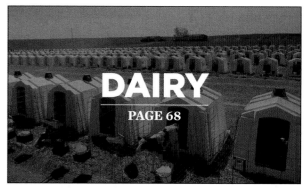

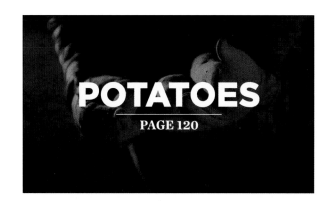
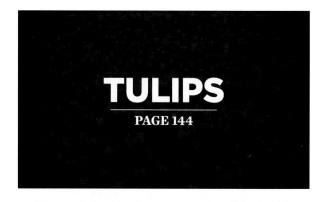

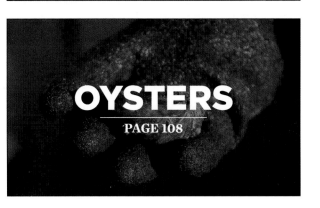

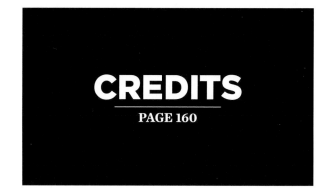

APPLES

Apples are Washington state's No. 1 crop. The industry was built on an apple that is lipstick red and fit for a teacher's desk. And while the Red Delicious remains an important mainstay, consumer tastes have shifted and orchardists have responded with varieties to keep Washington on top.

Staying on top will not be easy. A big concern for the industry is the loss of family farms. About a decade ago, there were 4,000 independent apple growers in Washington. Today there are 1,450. That trend isn't unique to apple growers.

Across the state, midsize farms are being stamped out by economic and social pressure. The apple industry highlights some of the reasons for an increasingly consolidated industry.

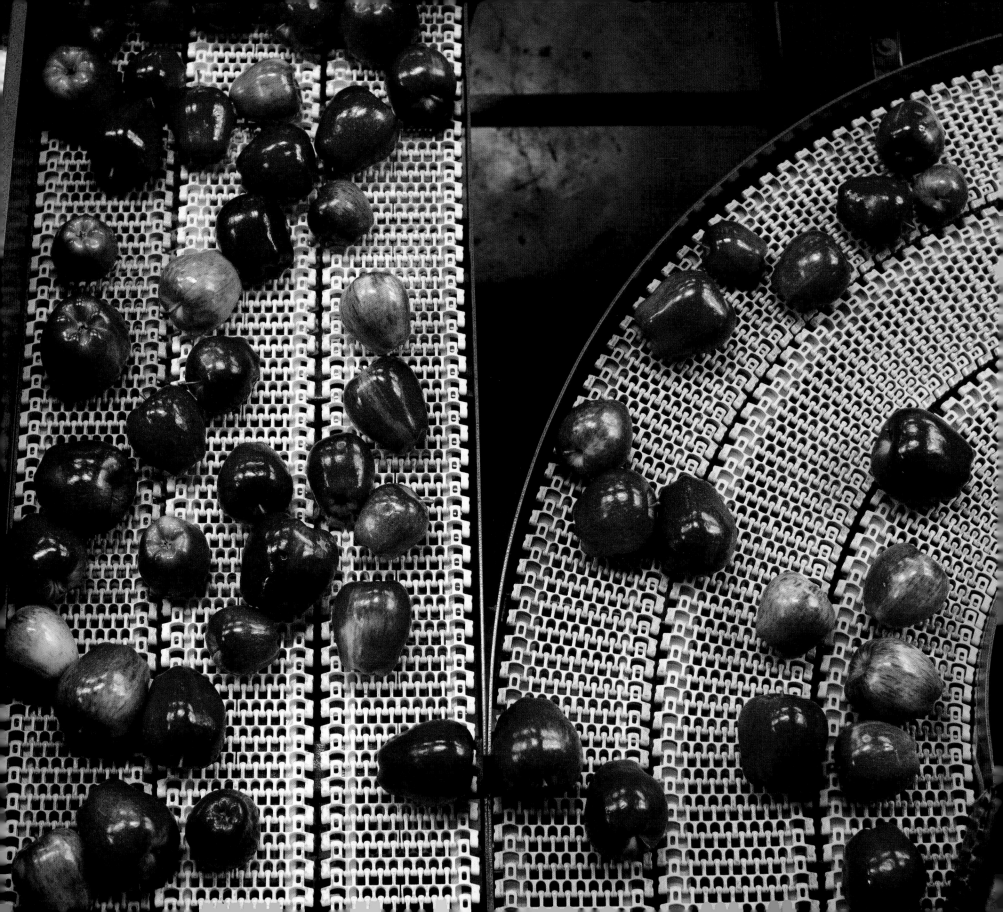

ADAPTING IS CORE TO CROP

Midsize orchard farmers struggle to compete with big industry

Story by Eli Francovich, photos by Tyler Tjomsland

THE SPOKESMAN-REVIEW

CHELAN, Wash. — On a rainy day in the hills above Lake Chelan, Dave Robison is checking on his blossoming apple trees.

Days earlier he had sprayed the trees across his 120-acre orchard to cull some blossoms, leaving only the hardiest.

It's a job Robison remembers doing with his dad. Before that, it was a job his grandfather first started doing in the Chelan area in the late 1950s. Now, it's a task he carries out with his 27-year-old son.

But midsize apple orchards like the Robisons' are disappearing.

About a decade ago, there were 4,000 independent apple growers in Washington. Today there are 1,450, according to Todd Fryhover, president of the Washington Apple Commission.

That trend isn't unique to apple growers.

Across the state, midsize farms are being stamped out by economic and social pressure. The apple industry, the state's top crop, highlights some of the reasons for an increasingly consolidated industry.

"I know more than one farmer who is still farming real hard and they're 80 years old," Robison said. "There are too many parts of it that are outside our control."

"You can be the best farmer in the world and still go broke," he said.

The industry and the culture

In early May, thousands of people lined the streets of downtown Wenatchee to watch the Stemilt Growers 98th Washington State Apple Blossom Festival Grand Parade.

A pink and silver, tinsel-covered, apple-shaped structure sat on the lead float. Two teenagers, the apple blossom queen and princess, waved as spectators clapped.

"Someone in your world is involved in the apple industry. That's how it is here," said Darci Christoferson. "You're somehow committed to the apple industry."

Christoferson is the Apple Blossom Festival organizer and a former queen.

Christoferson said 100,000 people will attend the 11-day festival, with its parade, car show and other events, designed to celebrate the blossoming of the state's dominant agricultural crop.

Outlying towns create their own floats. The parade, which lasted about an hour and a half, featured high school marching bands, victorious high school sports teams and 4-H clubs.

"I always say Apple Blossom is kind of a family reunion," Christoferson said.

Wenatchee's moniker? Apple Capital of the World.

A day prior to the parade, Bob Bossen drove along the outskirts of Wenatchee. Stopping his truck in the middle of the road, he pointed toward a half-built subdivision. The sprouting houses are being built on former orchard land.

"Field men are probably the worst drivers in the world, because we're always gawking at orchards," he said.

But more and more, what he's pointing at isn't an orchard — it's a housing development.

> "Field men are probably the worst drivers in the world, because we're always gawking at orchards."
>
> — *Bob Bossen*

Bossen has been a horticulturist for 45 years. His grandfather owned apple orchards, as did his father. But Bossen sold his land — about 15 acres — to a larger grower when his children weren't interested in continuing the business.

Now he works for the Northern Fruit Company, helping to keep the orchards healthy. The industry has changed, he said. Fewer and fewer young people are interested in getting into an increasingly competitive and difficult business.

"There has been a lot of consolidation in our industry," said the apple commission's Fryhover. "It is continuing to happen, and I think you see that in all agriculture."

Higher yields, better technology, fewer farmers

Data from the United States Department of Agriculture's census shows a decrease in midsize farms in Washington. In 1997, there were 8,446 farms between 50 and 219 acres in size.

In 2012, there were 7,276 farms that size.

It's the same story across the nation. According to a

OPPOSITE: Red Delicious apples make their way to packing boxes. There were 39 million boxes of Red Delicious packed in Washington in 2017.

WASHINGTON APPLE SAMPLER

RED DELICIOUS

39 million boxes packed last year

Once heralded for its shape, color and uniformity, the iconic Red Delicious has fallen from favor. It may remain the single largest variety in Washington, but sweeter, crisper apples are earning consumer preference.

GALA

31.5 million boxes packed

The sweet apple developed in New Zealand is a lunch-sack favorite. They were introduced 52 years ago and have steadily gained market share and orchardist allegiance.

FUJI

17.5 million boxes packed

The apple from Japan is among the sweetest on grocery shelves. The Fuji is large, round and blushed. It's a quick fix for a sweet-tooth snack and is a popular variety as a salad topper.

GRANNY SMITH

15.8 million boxes packed

The Granny Smith is the most popular of the tart apples coveted by pie makers and snackers. Introduced in 1868, this Australian apple is smaller, green and believed to be descended in part from crabapples.

HONEYCRISP

8.3 million boxes packed

Unleashed by University of Minnesota researchers 26 years ago, the Honeycrisp apple became a crowd favorite. It's not overly sweet. Nor is it especially tart. It has a mottled skin and is good for just about everything, from snacking to turning into applesauce.

THE SPOKESMAN-REVIEW

2014 article by Daniel Sumner, a professor of agricultural and resource economics at the University of California, Davis, the size of commercial farms has more than doubled in the past 20 years.

"Commercial agriculture in the United States is comprised of several hundred thousand farms, and these farms continue to become larger and fewer," Sumner writes in the conclusion of the article.

The Washington apple industry is no different. In the past 10 years, the number of independent growers has dropped from 4,000 to 1,450, a 63 percent decrease, even though the overall acreage is about the same.

Robison said that decrease is due to the unique nature of the apple business. On average, apple farmers might get 40 bins per acre, while some growers are producing more and others produce less.

"You take wheat, everybody basically produces the same," Robison said. "But in tree fruit some guys can be making three or four times more than the others."

Part of what makes the increased productivity possible is new technology and orchard planting systems. However, implementing those systems can be cost prohibitive for small operations.

Once those systems are in place and orchardists become more efficient, the gap widens between large and small.

"It's never been like it is right now, never," Robison said.

Karina Gallardo, a professor at Washington State who studies the economics of tree fruit, said several factors are leading to consolidation.

The first, she said, is the rising costs of starting an orchard or breaking into the business.

There's also the time element: It can take a long time for farmers to get paid for their crop.

She's also seen an increase in the cost of storing, packing, shipping and marketing fruit. And at the end of the tree-to-table process, it's difficult for midsize farmers to negotiate with consolidated retailing.

Gallardo hasn't studied the issue of consolidation.

Instead, she relies on what she has been told and observed.

Robison also attributes the consolidation to increasing government regulations.

"It's just mind-boggling, the regulations that come up. When a big company comes across a new regulation, if they have to, they can hire somebody who can (navigate) it," Robison said. "But as small farmers, we just have to deal with it all."

Mark Powers, the president of the Northwest Horticultural Council, said increased oversight usually means increased costs.

"All of that drives costs," he said. "If you're a small grower, it's very difficult to pay for the expertise, basically the full-time attention that is required to be in compliance to all of these requirements."

Fryhover is quick to point out that Washington's apple industry remains dominated by family-owned enterprises, from the orchards to the packing plants. However, those family operations are becoming large businesses.

Isabel Vega, 65, works to prune apple trees in an orchard near Chelan, Wash. "People see beauty here," she said. "I see work, but in my life I have worked to live."

"These people have been around a long time and they are vertically integrated," he said.

When one family company owns the orchards, packing plant, and distribution and sales organization, they can absorb costs more easily, Robison said. That increases the speed with which the industry evolves.

When considering his son's future as a farmer, Robison is realistic.

"I think there is a 50-50 chance (he'll retire as a farmer)," he said. "We've talked about that."

Still a big player

Fryhover understands why people might think the apple industry had lost some of its luster. With fewer individual farmers, the direct, daily impact of the business might be lost on some.

"When you think of Washington, you think of Boeing and Microsoft and Amazon," he said.

And although technology and manufacturing jobs may dominate the west side of the state, he said the apple industry continues to play a vital role in the state's economy.

In 2015, the state's apple industry was worth $2.04 billion. That's 22 percent of the state's total agricultural value, according to the United States Department of Agriculture. Nationally, the 2015 crop represented 59.9 percent of the country's apple production.

A profit puzzle piece

Across the lake from Robison's home near the small town of Manson, Phylis Gleasman has been growing apples since 1981. That's when she moved with her husband back to the Chelan area and jumped into the apple business. Her husband died in 2005, and Gleasman farms her 60 or so acres with the help of her son, who also works as a schoolteacher.

Her orchards are high in the hills above the long, narrow lake, right at the edge of where apples can grow, she said. Nowadays those hills are increasingly dotted with housing developments.

"As the rural area disappears and becomes more urban, there are challenges," she said.

Neighbors expect rural peace and quiet, and are unhappy when farm machinery makes noise, she said. One neighbor recently sued her, claiming that when she sprayed her orchards, the chemicals drifted onto their property. The lawsuit is ongoing, but to appease them, she built a 30-foot-tall barrier between the orchard and their property.

When Gleasman started farming, she was unusual — one of the few people who "didn't inherit" a family business, she said.

"We started from scratch," she said.

Things have changed since then. With the increased price and complexity of the apple business, Gleasman isn't sure she could start out in the same manner today.

But she prides herself on adapting to those changes.

"You can't look at this (like it's) 20 years ago," she said. "You have to look at this strictly as a business. You can't just go out there and sit on a tractor with a piece of straw in your mouth."

Now she's constantly looking ahead, figuring out ways she can make her business more efficient, while simultaneously planting the kinds of apples consumers want. It's a tricky balancing act.

When Gleasman and Robison started farming, the Washington apple industry was dominated by one variety, Red Delicious. Consumers' tastes changed, however, fueled by the introduction of new, tastier varieties: Gala, Fuji, and Honeycrisp, to name three.

The varieties are good for discerning consumers, but makes the farmers' jobs harder. Instead of relying on one, homogeneous crop, they have to plant multiple varieties, hoping that one or two will be popular when they start producing.

Trees themselves have to be ordered three years in advance. And once planted, they take about five years to reach full yield, Gleasman said.

"You just hope that dart hits the target, that you're getting something profitable," she said.

In mid-May, Gleasman is in the middle of planting a new section of orchard. She's bought Red Delicious trees, but plans to graft the more profitable Sugar Bee apples onto the Red Delicious root stalk.

In addition to planting new varieties, farmers are also planting narrower rows to accommodate shorter, denser orchards. In the past there would be 300 to 400 apple trees per acre. Now, with changes in technology and horticulture, farmers can get 1,500 to 2,000 trees per acre, Fryhover said. And those trees are shorter, with fruit hanging just 8 feet off the ground.

Already, many orchards are harvesting fruit using motorized platforms, removing the need for tall and dangerous ladders.

The next big thing? Automated harvest. The technology is still in development, but many orchardists hope it will see widespread use in Washington within 10 years. Automating harvest would remove one of the industry's biggest and most persistent challenges — labor costs.

"Yes, there is a lot of interest in it (automation)," Fryhover said. "The labor is just the tough, tough part."

But, as with all innovations in the industry, automated harvest will cost money and take time to implement. For a robot to accurately and efficiently pick fruit, the orchard has to be uniform.

"So you have to have the orchard structure first when you talk about automation," Fryhover said. "And that's not cheap. You're talking about $40,000 to $50,000 an acre to plant an orchard like this."

'If we play our cards right'

Gleasman's operation is also a family affair. Her son, the schoolteacher, works nights, weekends and summers.

Touring her orchards, she greets her grandson, Luke Gleasman, who is driving a tractor while Jose Perez places trees in the furrowed earth. Lake Chelan glimmers in the distance.

"Hey, big buddy," Gleasman says to Luke, who plays football at Carroll College in Montana and is home visiting for a few weeks.

Gleasman doesn't worry much about the future. She thinks that as long as she continues to adapt and respond, there is a way for midsize farms to succeed.

"We are constantly reinvesting in our orchard to make sure it is farmed right and it has quality diversification," she said.

And while Robison is more concerned than Gleasman, he also thinks there is a future.

It just won't be easy.

"I know that us small farmers, if we play our cards right, there is always going to be room for us," he said. "We can micromanage. We don't have the money to make changes real fast, but we can micromanage what we have."

> **"As the rural area disappears and becomes more urban, there are challenges."**
>
> — *Phylis Gleasman*

OPPOSITE: Newer housing developments, like this one in Wenatchee, Wash., are squeezing out apple orchards.

From apples to wheat, NAFTA has been a boon for Washington state agriculture

Story by Eli Francovich, photo by Tyler Tjomsland

THE SPOKESMAN-REVIEW

For Washington apples, the North American Free Trade Agreement has been a good deal.

The agreement has allowed apples grown in Central Washington to travel, unfettered and untaxed, down to Mexico and up to Canada.

Exports to the two countries have created more than 4,000 jobs and the international exposure has boosted Washington's reputation as the apple state.

"These kind of agreements give us a leg up," said Rebecca Lyons, international marketing director for the Washington State Apple Commission. "You know, one of the challenges we have here is we are a higher-cost producer and our competitors in many of these markets are not."

Lyons said prior to NAFTA's implementation in 1994, Washington exported some apples to Mexico and Canada, but high tariffs made it a costly endeavor.

Now, between 7 and 9 percent of Washington's apple crop goes to Mexico.

"We have full access. There are no duties," said Todd Fryhover, the president of the Washington Apple Commission. "It's a year-round market. It really is perfect the way that it is."

And the benefit isn't limited to apples.

Mark Powers, the president of the Northwest Horticultural Council, said 20 percent of the pear crop and 15 percent of the apple crop go to Mexico or Canada. The export business alone generates about $500 million per year, he said.

Any withdrawal from NAFTA would shake the Washington apple industry to its core.

In May 2017, President Donald Trump announced plans to renegotiate the deal, seemingly stepping back from campaign promises to withdraw the United States completely from the agreement.

During the campaign, Trump called the deal "the worst trade deal in the history of the world."

Nationally, farmers and farmer associations expressed

Caesar Lopez works in one of Phyllis Gleasman's orchards to plant new apple trees in Manson, Wash.

concern at the potential renegotiation. Powers, however, said he is not worried.

"I think that there is room for renegotiation and improvement," he said.

However, any changes need to keep agriculture's best interest in mind. Especially important, he said, is to not impose any tariffs on Mexican goods, which could start a trade war.

Prior to NAFTA, Powers said, there was a 20 percent tariff on any Washington tree fruit going to Mexico. The removal of that cost has led to a 70 percent increase in exports.

"I know there are concerns related to manufacturing goods and that kind of thing," Powers said.

He hopes that whatever is put in place to protect manufacturing interests doesn't "harm agriculture interests."

Since 1994, annual farm exports to Mexico have increased five-fold to about $18 billion. Mexico is the No. 3 market for U.S. agriculture.

Apple growers in Washington stood to benefit from the Trans-Pacific Partnership, so when Trump withdrew the U.S. from the deal in January, Powers said it was a "disappointment."

It was particularly damaging to the effort to open up the Vietnam apple market, he said. Still, Washington already has decent access to Asian markets, although there are tariffs.

And Washington's focus on Asia won't change.

"That's the growth area in this world," Powers said. "Our industry is focused in Asia and the growing middle class."

Dave Robison, a midsize apple farmer, said he didn't notice a huge change when NAFTA went into affect in 1994. He hopes Trump reduces regulations on agriculture, but for the most part, he said, he doesn't pay too much attention to politics.

"As a full-time farmer, I'm pretty far removed," he said.

The Associated Press contributed to this report.

The farmers' workaround: Tree grafting

Story by Eli Francovich
THE SPOKESMAN-REVIEW

Planting a modern apple orchard is expensive work costing between $40,000 and $50,000 per acre. What's more, the kinds of apples people want to eat can change. That means an orchard planted this year might not be that valuable by the time it has reached full maturity five years later.

One way apple farmers in Washington can adapt to changing tastes? Grafting. It's an ancient process that melds two different types of apple trees together. Simply put, the stem of one variety's leaf buds are inserted into the stalk of the tree.

Grafting isn't cheap — it costs about $1,000 per acre. But it's cheaper than replanting, and it's one way for farmers to adapt relatively quickly to changing markets.

CLEFT GRAFT: CHANGING A TREE FROM RED DELICIOUS TO HONEYCRISP

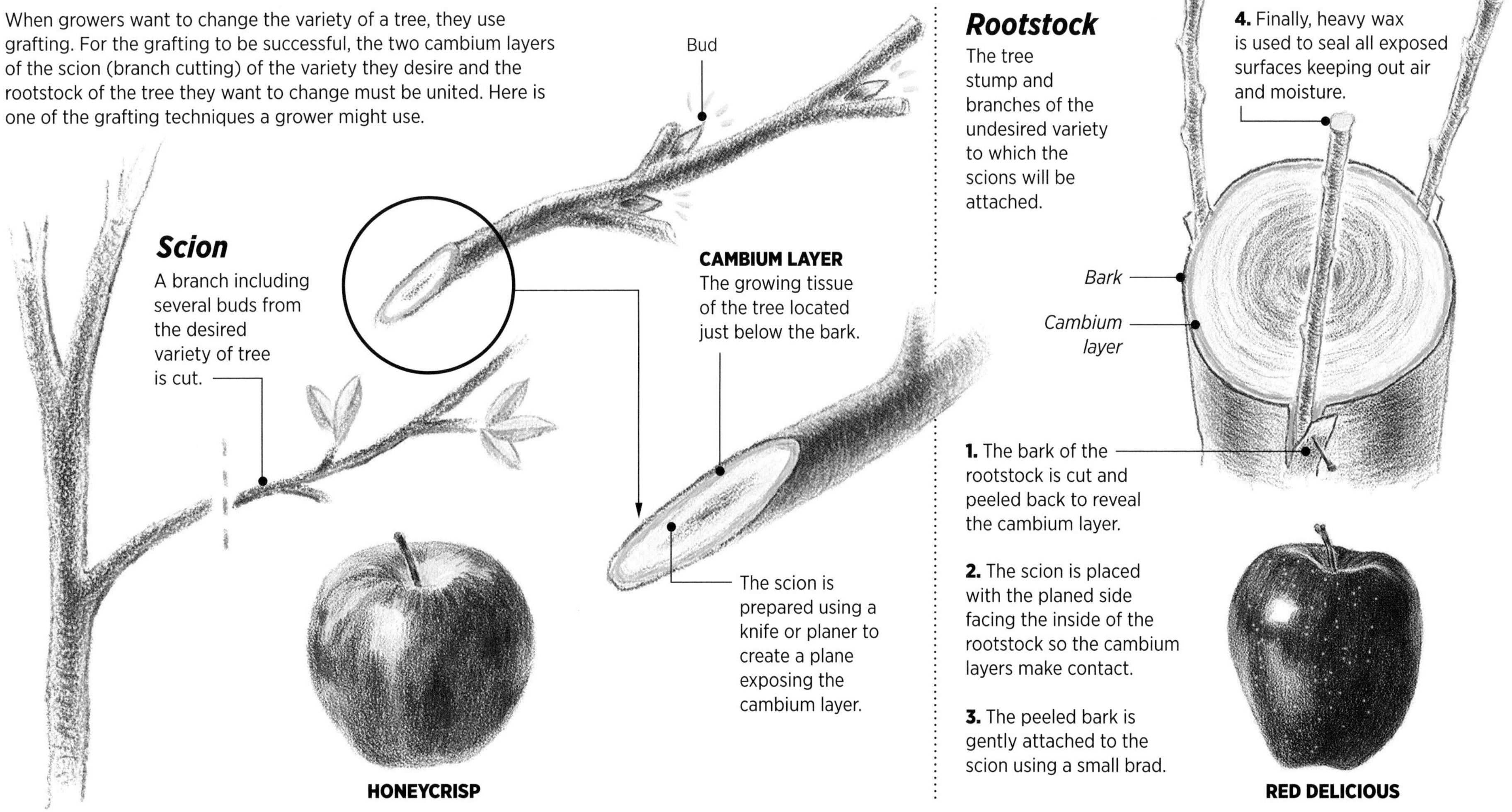

When growers want to change the variety of a tree, they use grafting. For the grafting to be successful, the two cambium layers of the scion (branch cutting) of the variety they desire and the rootstock of the tree they want to change must be united. Here is one of the grafting techniques a grower might use.

Bud

Scion
A branch including several buds from the desired variety of tree is cut.

CAMBIUM LAYER
The growing tissue of the tree located just below the bark.

The scion is prepared using a knife or planer to create a plane exposing the cambium layer.

HONEYCRISP

Rootstock
The tree stump and branches of the undesired variety to which the scions will be attached.

4. Finally, heavy wax is used to seal all exposed surfaces keeping out air and moisture.

Bark

Cambium layer

1. The bark of the rootstock is cut and peeled back to reveal the cambium layer.

2. The scion is placed with the planed side facing the inside of the rootstock so the cambium layers make contact.

3. The peeled bark is gently attached to the scion using a small brad.

RED DELICIOUS

Source: Washington State University Extension

MOLLY QUINN/THE SPOKESMAN-REVIEW

ASPARAGUS

Washington is one of the nation's largest asparagus growers. Fresh-cut spears from Adams, Benton, Franklin, Grant, Walla Walla and Yakima counties end up in grocery stores throughout the U.S. and Canada. Frozen spears from the same fields are also delivered to doorsteps across the country through companies such as Schwan's. And asparagus that's been cut and pickled outside Pasco can be purchased in 16- and 32-ounce jars at Costco. This report explores the rise in production and reasons for optimism about the future of asparagus farming in Washington.

STALKS RISING

Trade deals just about spoiled Washington's asparagus industry. Farmers quit the crop. Canneries closed.
Then, slowly, farmers used technology and grit to create a second chance.

Story by Adriana Janovich, photos by Jesse Tinsley

THE SPOKESMAN-REVIEW

YAKIMA VALLEY, Wash. — Maribel Teran works quickly and methodically. She doesn't like to take breaks. The faster she works, the more asparagus she cuts. The more asparagus she cuts, the more money she makes.

But the basket on her hip weighs about 15 pounds when it's full.

"It's heavy," she said.

The first couple of weeks, she really feels it. In her legs. In her back. Her muscles are stiff from stooping. "You get sore," she said. "Many people, they quit."

Harvesting asparagus hurts. Each spear is hand-cut with a quick jab of a long knife that ends with a notched "V" tip designed to clip stalks below the soil. So asparagus cutters spend most of the harvest with their backs bent in fields throughout the Columbia Basin and Yakima Valley.

Teran is one of the best cutters at Inaba Produce Farms, which owns asparagus fields west of Wapato. The company supplies the fresh-cut tender green shoots to high-end grocers, such as PCC Natural Markets in the Seattle area and New Seasons Markets in Oregon, California and the west side of Washington.

Sometimes, as her knife slices through the base of a single spear, Teran said she wonders, "Who's going to eat this asparagus?"

Washington is one of the nation's largest asparagus growers. Fresh-cut spears from Adams, Benton, Franklin,

Grant, Walla Walla and Yakima counties end up in grocery stores throughout the U.S. and Canada. Frozen spears from the same fields also are delivered to doorsteps across the country through companies such as Schwan's. And asparagus that's been cut and pickled outside Pasco can be purchased in 16- and 32-ounce jars at Costco.

Production has been on the rise in recent years, and there are reasons for optimism about the future of asparagus farming in Washington. New technology and growing practices are making it more efficient at a time when Americans are eating more fresh asparagus.

The industry, said Alan Schreiber, director of the Washington Asparagus Commission, seems to be on the cusp of what could be considered a new age for Washington asparagus.

"We are not like any other crop," he said. "The way it's handled. The way it's grown."

And, perhaps more important, "No one else has the quality Washington has."

Yet the Washington asparagus industry remains a shadow of its former self. Production is about 80 percent less than what it was in 1990, when Washington was the world's leading producer of green asparagus.

Today, the crop faces competition from foreign markets that weren't major players three decades ago — Peru and Mexico, in particular — as well as ever-present concerns about rising labor costs and a shrinking labor force.

While the demand for fresh asparagus is rising, industry experts agree Washington asparagus production will never return to previous levels, when canning was king.

At the industry's peak in 1990, Washington produced 102 million pounds of asparagus grown on 30,000 acres. A year later, the U.S. enacted the Andean Trade Preference Act,

allowing Peruvian asparagus — heavily subsidized by the U.S. government — to enter America tariff-free. Canneries closed and moved to Peru.

Today, Washington grows 22 million pounds on 4,400 acres.

The numbers, Schreiber said, "are pretty stunning." They show, he said, the collapse of an industry. The low point was 2013, when Washington asparagus farmers produced 15.8 million pounds, or about 15 percent of what was grown in 1990.

"There's no comeback for canned asparagus," Schreiber said. "I doubt we will see Washington ever returning to being a largely processed-asparagus industry. We're not going to go back to the way it was."

The focus now is on fresh.

The same year Washington asparagus growers hit an all-time low in production, Schreiber, in his annual state-of-the-industry address, encouraged them to plant more.

"We are not planting enough asparagus to make our industry as competitive as it needs to be," he said that year. "It is time to start planting asparagus."

If they didn't plant more and change things, Schreiber told the growers, the Washington asparagus industry "would no longer be viable."

Four years later, it's working.

Growers are switching to new varieties and trying different planting techniques. They've adopted more intensive management methods, as well as increased automation in packing sheds. And, for the first time since 1990, Schreiber said, they're "planting more than they are taking out."

Washington asparagus is emerging as a "more competitive" industry with "more aggressive" marketing, he said. Yields are increasing. One new acre now can produce double what an old acre produced.

"No one has the yields we have," Schreiber said, noting this year's harvest is projected to be more than that of either Michigan or California.

"Buyers recognize Washington quality," Schreiber said. "We get paid a premium over everybody else," including Peru and Mexico, Michigan and California.

"In a sense, the Washington asparagus (industry) is back," Schreiber said. "But it is not your father's asparagus industry."

It even has its own hashtag: #GetFreshWithUs.

Crowning glory

Once classified as a lily, asparagus thrives in well-drained, sandy, alkaline soil. It evolved around the Mediterranean Sea, growing from Spain to Syria and dating to ancient times. Ancient Greeks, Romans and Egyptians ate fresh asparagus.

It's difficult to pinpoint when asparagus farming started in Washington. Schreiber, head of the state asparagus commission since 2002, said it's been cultivated in the Columbia Basin for at least the past 110 years. He knows this, he said, because he has a photo that's dated 1907 and portrays Columbia Basin farmers with the delicate, quick-growing crop.

Asparagus can grow anywhere from 5 to 7 — and even 9 — inches in one day during warm weather. To keep up, cutters must harvest spears daily. Harvesting is done entirely by hand. Cutters bend at the waist, positioning their knives at a 45-degree angle, pivoting between rows at a quick clip, sharpening their blades on the go and watching where they step. They must take care to not damage the spears.

The perennial plant has a short shelf life and is best enjoyed while it's young. Once the tips start budding, or "ferning out," the stalks quickly become tough and fibrous.

The season is short but intense. It generally starts in early April and runs through mid-June. This year, because of cooler weather, it began about two weeks late.

Harvest typically runs 65 to 70 straight days. "It's not religious," Schreiber said. "It does not observe the Sabbath."

Cutters harvest spears one by one until they have a handful. They trim the woody ends with a single slash of their long-handled knives and tuck the spears into the box at their hips.

"It's stoop labor. It's hard work," Schreiber said. "I'd like to see you finish a row."

Teran, 27, cuts on a two-person crew with her boyfriend, Nivardo Santiago, 26. Together, they tackle 72 half-rows,

> "
>
> ## "We are not like any other crop. The way it's handled. The way it's grown."
>
> *— Alan Schreiber*

TAKING STALK: ASPARAGUS PRIMER

FRESH

Fresh asparagus makes up most of the global asparagus market — about 74 percent— and it's expected to remain that way. Longer spears — stretching 8 and 9 inches — are desired for sales of fresh asparagus.

WHITE

White asparagus is one of the more labor-intensive vegetables to grow. Farmers grow and harvest the spears underground to keep them from producing chlorophyll, which turns them green. While demand is slowly increasing in the U.S., it remains highest in Europe.

PURPLE

Purple asparagus looks striking on the shelf or table at the farmer's market. It makes up a small percentage of the market and remains a novelty. But the color doesn't last: purple asparagus turns green when you cook it.

PICKLED

Shorter spears are used for pickled asparagus. The delicacy makes a great addition to a bloody mary, and you can buy a three-pack of 32-ounce Foster's Pickled Asparagus — grown and pickled outside of Pasco — for $29 on Amazon.

FROZEN

Shorter spears are also used for frozen asparagus. Schwan's, for example, uses Washington-grown asparagus and features 6-inch stalks.

THE SPOKESMAN-REVIEW

Before a panorama that includes Mount Adams, asparagus cutters pause to empty their buckets into plastic boxes in a field at Inaba Produce Farms in the Yakima Valley. The work is backbreaking and tedious, but skilled cutters can make good money through the two-month harvest, which is seven days a week.

or the equivalent of 31 regular rows. Most cutters harvest 12 to 16 full rows, or about 2 acres, in a four- to six-hour workday.

Crews of generally two to five or six people — often fighting the darkness with light from headlamps — cut out morning glory, thistle and other weeds as they care for the same section every day.

"Everybody has their own number and their own area," said Norm Inaba, who owns this farm with his family. "The way you cut dictates what the next day will be. A good cutter makes the asparagus better. A bad cutter will make the asparagus bad."

'It just shoots up'

Teran and Nivardo are two of his best. They're in his organic field near Harrah by 5 a.m., sometimes earlier, to start cutting before the break of dawn, when it's still cool. They must assess every spear, deciding — based on length and appearance — whether to cut, cull or leave it for tomorrow.

Long and straight spears are prized. Crooked ones are culled. So are the skinny ones, which pull nutrients from the wider, weightier and more desired spears.

It's difficult to keep up, especially when the weather's warm.

"You return the next day and it looks like a different field," Inaba said. "It just shoots up."

Cutters empty their baskets as they go, placing spears into larger boxes set at the end of their rows. Those boxes are picked up by truck and taken to a packing line. Inaba packs his own. But most farmers take their asparagus to a nearby plant for packing or processing into pickled or frozen products.

About two dozen growers bring asparagus — anywhere from 20 to 1,200, even 1,500, boxes a day — to Johnson Foods in Sunnyside, where spears are washed, weighed, measured, graded and sorted by size: jumbo, extra large, large, medium and small.

Within three days, the spears ship throughout the Pacific

As dawn breaks over the Yakima Valley farm of the Inaba family, workers begin to spread out in their respective fields.

Northwest and as far away as New York. They leave the plant, bound for shelves at Fred Meyer, Safeway and Costco — and, eventually, people's plates.

Teran thinks about them sometimes. She wonders if they ever think about who cut the particular spears they're consuming.

After a four- or five-hour stint in the organic field at Inaba Produce Farms, where they're paid by the pound, Teran and Nivardo move onto a conventional field at the same farm, where they're paid an hourly wage. Many asparagus cutters work double shifts to make more

money during the fierce but fleeting season.

Experienced asparagus cutters can make up to $30 an hour. The industry average, Schreiber said, is $15 to $20. At the very least, farmworkers make minimum wage, which in Washington is $11, one of the highest in the country.

Teran moved to the United States from Mexico City when she was 15. None of the faces in the fields where she works are white. Cutters here have varied ethnic backgrounds: Mexican, Guatemalan and Haitian are common.

Like Teran, many work other crops within Washington's

rich agricultural industry. Apples, sweet corn, green beans and grapes need people for the harvests throughout the summer and fall. Asparagus, which she's been harvesting since finishing high school, is hardest. But it's her favorite. "I make more money here."

After two or three weeks in the asparagus fields, her body becomes used to the bending, and, she said, "I feel nothing."

Still, asparagus season takes its toll. Teran usually loses weight during harvest, "maybe 10 pounds," she said.

She finishes in the fields around 2 or 3 p.m. and is

usually in bed before 10 p.m.. She wakes around 3:30 a.m. to make lunch — sometimes tacos or tortas or tostadas. She likes asparagus, too. Her preparation of the slender, tender, labor-intensive vegetable is simple. She likes it with eggs or with butter, cooked "just in the microwave."

Inaba encourages Teran to save money for college. She wants to go. Or, maybe, beauty school. But she's also saving money to support her mom, who was in a car accident on her way to come to work in the fields.

The same fields drew Inaba's grandfather from Japan in 1907. He sees a comparison between the workers in his fields and his own immigrant ancestors. Whether they arrived 110 years ago or in the recent past, Inaba said, "Everyone came here for one reason: for a better life."

Deep roots

Inaba and his two older brothers and business partners, Lon and Wayne, are third-generation farmers with deep roots in the Yakima Valley, once the epicenter of asparagus production in Washington.

When they were growing up here in the 1960s and '70s, they would hunt for errant asparagus spears, sprouted from seeds spread by birds and the wind. "My grandmother and I and all us kids would pick it on the ditch bank," Norm Inaba said.

The Inaba brothers didn't get into asparagus until 1988, beginning with about 20 acres. "A lot of other people were growing it, and we wanted to grow something different," Norm Inaba said.

Today, he and his brothers farm 250 acres of asparagus. It accounts for about one-sixth of all of their crops. It also takes three or four years to mature.

Planting is Year Zero. In Year One, a grower generally gets five to 10 days of cutting, Inaba said. Year Two, maybe 10 to 30. Year Three usually yields a full or nearly full harvest. Year Four is a mature crop.

It's an investment that takes time, money and patience to earn a return. The plant's root masses, or crowns, are typically planted in March beneath 7 to 9 inches of soil and 60 inches apart. Farmers need about 2,600 crowns per acre. At a cost of about $100 per 1,000 crowns, that's $2,600 per acre. Add in the cost of field prep and labor, and it's about $3,500 just to plant 1 acre of asparagus, Schreiber said.

Lately, farmers have been experimenting with tighter rows, planting crowns 40 inches apart, for larger yields. Some also have started direct seeding and trying new varieties, such as Guelph Millennium — which "right now is the rock star," Schreiber said.

Inaba also sees opportunity in the organic market. He has 50 acres of organic asparagus, plus another 40 acres in transition to become organic. In all, Schreiber estimated, Washington has some 200 acres of organic asparagus.

People are experimenting with purple, too. There are about four farmers in the state growing a combined total of about 20 acres of purple asparagus, Schreiber said. People pay more for it because it looks dramatic and quantities are limited. But that might change, just like the industry.

These days, some 70 percent of Washington's asparagus growers are located in the Columbia Basin, which is closer to Walla Walla and Dayton, where the canneries once processed the harvest. It's also where bigger fields with larger capacities for production were available.

Gourmet Trading Co., the biggest fresh asparagus plant in America, spans 85,000 square feet outside Pasco, where the company has about 445 acres of asparagus.

Phil Clouse, 73, oversees them.

"I really think that Gourmet has really added some stability to the fresh market in this state," he said, rolling through the company's uniform, undulating fields in the red 2011 Ford F-150 he refers to as "my office."

The soil is sandy loam and the yields are way above average. Farmers are shooting for 15,000 pounds per acre or more, or three times the average. And cutters here are making more than $20 per hour.

"Asparagus has probably sent more kids to college than any other crop," said Clouse, who's been in the business more than 40 years.

"People just go crazy for it," he said. "It's a sign of spring."

Gourmet's operation is a sign of something, too.

"This is the future of asparagus," Clouse said. "Right here."

Schreiber, sitting in the cab of Clouse's truck, agrees. "I'm very much in awe of this operation. I have a lot of respect for it. But part of me doesn't want this to be the future of asparagus. This is a multinational corporation. It's going to be very hard for the littler grower to keep up."

'Fresh is better'

To help the entire industry, the commission launched a limited marketing campaign in 2015, including starting a Facebook page. Today, it has more than 800 "likes." More concentrated efforts started last year.

"Growing asparagus has gotten more challenging," said Inaba, who's a board member for the commission. "It's kind of an experiment. If you can't adjust, you die. You have to adapt."

The Inabas' first full asparagus crop was ready right around the same year the trade agreement took effect, crushing the state's canned asparagus industry and flooding the fresh market. Farmers plowed under asparagus fields. Some replanted with other crops. Others walked away.

"I saw a lot of friends and other people who had to leave when the Del Monte plant and the Green Giant plant closed," Inaba said. "I don't think we'll see 30,000 acres again. I just don't. There's just a few growers now."

Inaba encourages consumers to support the ones who are left. He advises them to check labels for "Washington grown." He also advises them not to buy asparagus on sight alone.

"It will tell you when it's old," he said. "Pick it up and smell it. If it doesn't smell good, put it back and walk away."

Inaba likes his asparagus grilled with olive oil and Johnny's Seasoning Salt. His wife prefers Montreal Steak Seasoning. She also prepares it with butter, garlic salt and Parmesan.

Either way, "It's hard to beat fresh asparagus," he said. "Fresh is better."

"
"This is a multinational corporation. It's going to be hard for the littler grower to keep up. "

— Alan Schreiber

Thousands of stalks of asparagus poke up from the fertile dirt of the Yakima Valley at Inaba Produce Farms fields near Harrah, Wash. The vegetable must be harvested every day, seven days a week for two months or more, so there is a dire need for experienced labor to cut the asparagus. JESSE TINSLEY / THE SPOKESMAN-REVIEW

About that 'disagreeable odour' ...

by Paul Turner
THE SPOKESMAN-REVIEW

Eating asparagus is good for you, but it can make your pee stink.

This awareness is not new.

In 1781, Benjamin Franklin wrote, "a few stems of asparagus eaten, shall give our urine a disagreeable odour."

No kidding, Ben.

But here's the thing. Apparently not everyone produces this telltale sulfurous smell (at least not to the same degree), and not everyone can detect it when it is present.

With the helpful guidance of John Fellman, a professor of plant physiology at Washington State University, a survey of the asparagus urine research suggests the following broad findings.

Some undetermined segment of the population produces the aroma. Some segment does not.

Some segment is predisposed to detect the odor, while another part of the general population does not detect it.

There may be a connection between producing the

aroma and being able to detect it.

So it comes down to a matter of production vs. perception. In any event, evidence suggests it's all a matter of genetic differences.

But for those who can smell that smell, the molecular science does not begin to describe what the nose knows.

Yakima County asparagus farmer Ron Granholm said the offending bouquet can be breathtaking.

"It's amazing what asparagus can do to your pee," he said. "It really stinks."

Amazing is certainly one word for it.

Smithsonian.com put it succinctly: "Our bodies convert asparagusic acid into sulfur-containing chemicals that stink."

The aroma is so pronounced some have been known to consider upcoming social engagements when deciding whether to consume asparagus.

You know, "Will I be a leading source of air pollution if

I eat asparagus now and use the bathroom at that party tonight?"

One asparagus-loving Spokane couple refers to the scent of the sour urine simply as "the problem."

Onset has been noted just mere minutes after dining on the vegetable in question.

But one study found 58 percent of men and 62 percent of women were unable to smell the funky asparagus aftereffect.

To those who can detect the odor, that must seem remarkable. Because when you can smell it, you can really smell it.

WSU's Fellman said that within the scientific community, this is largely viewed as a nonproblem. So a miracle cure likely is not in the offing, at least not anytime soon.

Meantime, some fans of asparagus will tell you the key to living in harmony with the succulent spears is a powerful bathroom fan.

How to kill a giant

Dayton lost its asparagus business to the "War on Drugs" but residents persevered

Story by Rachel Alexander
THE SPOKESMAN-REVIEW

DAYTON, Wash. — Nearly every lifelong resident has at least one story about the town's old asparagus cannery.

Ginny Butler, past president of the Dayton Historic Depot, remembers her mother and three friends took a job processing asparagus one summer to earn some extra spending money.

"They each wanted something for their house and their husbands didn't want to buy it," Butler said, laughing. Two of the women quit right away, but Butler's mother stuck it out, working grueling shifts while caring for her children.

By the end of the season, she was able to buy a decorative piece to hang over the family fireplace.

For decades, the plant defined life in Dayton. Each summer an influx of about 1,000 migrant workers would join the town's other 2,000 permanent residents. Hundreds more workers would tend the nearby fields.

And then it came to an abrupt stop. In 2005, the company moved much of its business to Peru, taking Washington's entire asparagus canning industry with it. Farmers plowed under fields. Two other canneries closed.

"It totally wiped us out. I've never seen such a huge, significant industry collapse," said Alan Schreiber, executive director of the Washington Asparagus Commission.

The culprit? Cocaine.

Growing a giant

The Green Giant cannery, as it would come to be called, opened in 1934 after a 45-day construction blitz, according to records from the Dayton Historic Depot. Workers processed peas from surrounding fields at first, then added asparagus in 1939. The company soon created a seed research department with a greenhouse to work on improving pea seeds, and set up a labor camp in 1942 to house Mexican-American workers from Texas.

The Minnesota Valley Canning Co. merged with Blue Mountain Canneries, Inc., the plant's original owner, in 1947.

By 1950, the company was called Green Giant.

In the early years, they packed asparagus grown in the Dayton area.

The crop, which is perennial, can grow for 15 years after a single planting, though shorter periods are more typical. Once it's done, farmers plow it up and plant something else.

Duane Dunlap, who started working as an agriculture personnel supervisor in 1966, said Green Giant would lease the fields from farmers for 20 years. When one cycle of asparagus was over, they'd move on to new land. By the 1970s, asparagus was migrating west, toward the Columbia Basin.

"Once the crop quit producing enough to be economical, you had to plow it up," he said. "Pretty soon we had no asparagus here."

Dunlap's job was to recruit migrant workers. In the early years, they were mostly single men, but by about 1972, he said, the plant started recruiting families.

Children sometimes worked in the fields with their parents before the company stopped that practice, requiring kids to go to school. Women often worked in the Dayton plant receiving asparagus from all over the region.

More than 40 years later, Dunlap can still recite the towns where the company kept workers housed: Starbuck,

A larger-than-life Jolly Green Giant still sits on the hillside above Dayton, Wash., though the plant that canned the company's asparagus left town for Peru in 2005. COLIN MULVANY / THE SPOKESMAN-REVIEW

Tucannon, Grandview, Kahlotus. Many cutters lived in Dayton and were bused out before sunrise to reach the fields, working until midday. The barracks in Dayton, recently donated to the county, sit on Green Giant Camp Road.

"It just mushroomed. We had asparagus fields all over the Columbia Basin," he said.

Mauricio Ramos started working in the asparagus fields around Dayton in 1975. His uncle began working around Dayton in 1942, when Texas migrant workers were bused up in the back of covered 10-wheeler trucks. By the time Ramos came from Eagle Pass, Texas, the workers traveled in buses with bathrooms.

Workers in the barracks woke at 4:30 a.m. and had to be ready to go to the fields by 5, Ramos said. Crews were driven to fields, about 20 miles outside of Dayton.

A 1983 filing with the U.S. Department of Labor calls for 150 plant workers, paid $4.26 per hour, or about $10.50 in today's dollars. Cutters made at least the federal minimum wage of $3.35 an hour, but earned $11.75 per hundred-weight of asparagus harvested.

"If you moved fast, it was good pay," Ramos said.

A 'war on drugs' casualty

As Washington's asparagus fields moved toward the

Tri-Cities, cocaine gripped American cities. Powdered cocaine was the king of drugs on Wall Street in the 1980s. Crack cocaine laid waste to the inner cities.

In a 1986 Gallup poll, 42 percent of Americans said crack and other forms of cocaine were the country's most serious drug problem, besting alcohol by eight percentage points.

This was the golden age of the War on Drugs, and officials in the other Washington came up with what they thought was a good solution: go after the source. So the United States signed the Andean Trade Preference Act, which went into effect in 1991. It gave trade preference via duty-free imports and grants to Andean countries that trafficked cocaine into the U.S.

The goal was to incentivize farmers to grow crops other than coca. The U.S. Agency for International Development built irrigation infrastructure and other projects in Peru. Farmers started planting asparagus.

Asparagus crowns take a few years to mature, and farmers needed time to get the crop right. The Washington market didn't start feeling the effects until about 2002, Schreiber said.

"Asparagus is not a hard crop to grow if you know how to grow it," he said. Once Peru developed that knowledge, Washington's canneries didn't have long.

Seneca Foods was the last in a string of Dayton plant owners who canned asparagus for Green Giant, which was then owned by General Mills. General Mills made the decision to move operations to Peru in 2005, citing Washington's high minimum wage and the lower cost of doing business in South America.

"They gutted the plant of all those machines and sent them to Peru," Dunlap said.

Dayton's plant was the last of three Washington asparagus canneries to close. In 2003, a Del Monte plant in Toppenish and another Seneca plant in Walla Walla stopped processing asparagus.

Mauricio Ramos started working in the asparagus fields around Dayton in 1975. He moved his family to Dayton after a few years in the fields, and eventually began doing irrigation work for the company. He left Green Giant in the early 1990s to take a job at City Lumber, a hardware store where he works today in downtown Dayton, Wash.
COLIN MULVANY / THE SPOKESMAN-REVIEW

Ramos moved his family to Dayton after a few years in the fields, and eventually began doing irrigation work for the company. He left Green Giant in the early 1990s to take a job at City Lumber, a hardware store in downtown Dayton. His wife spent about a decade in the plant, earning better wages than she could have gotten in Texas.

By the time he left Green Giant, Ramos said, rumors about the cannery's closure were always floating around. The asparagus fields had already moved out of Dayton further west.

"That year when they closed it, they didn't say anything. They just did it," he said.

Jennie Dickinson, now the Port of Columbia manager,

was the director of the Dayton Chamber of Commerce at the time of the closure. She said Seneca had been talking about Washington's minimum wage for a long time before the closure, saying they couldn't raise prices to make up the increased costs.

"You can only get so much for a can of asparagus," she said.

OPPOSITE: The Seneca seed processing plant in Dayton, Wash., employs about 50 locals now. When it was a asparagus processing plant, a local workforce of about 50 people swelled to more than 1,000 in the summer, as migrant workers, mostly from Texas, worked hunched over in summer heat to harvest the green spears.
COLIN MULVANY / THE SPOKESMAN-REVIEW

Peru deal a local bust

Cocaine still comes to the U.S. from Peru, though the amount of coca growing in the Andean highlands has fallen since the 1990s. Whether Peruvian asparagus production has helped depends on whom you ask.

The Peruvian government and White House drug policy office have both defended the trade preference, saying many asparagus farmers came from coca-producing regions.

Schreiber doesn't buy it. Coca is usually grown in the Andean highlands, while asparagus does best at sea level. A 2015 map by the Peruvian government showing hot spots for coca cultivation has almost no overlap with asparagus growing areas.

"They're the No. 1 exporter of coca and the No. 1 exporter of asparagus," Schreiber said.

That may not be strictly true — Colombian coca production surged in 2015, putting it ahead of Peru — but Peru has historically been and continues to be a major coca supplier.

USAID sent a little over $384 million in foreign aid to Peru in 2015, the most recent year for which complete data was available. About a third of that was spent on the Andean Counter Drug Program, and more on other law enforcement related to narcotics. Peru's agriculture sector got $24 million.

The amount of coca grown in Peru has fallen nearly 70 percent since 1992, according to data from the United Nations Office on Drugs and Crime. In 1992, farmers planted 129,100 hectares. By 2015, that was down to 40,300 hectares. A hectare is the equivalent of approximately 2½ acres.

But it's debatable whether that fall is because of asparagus. The largest reductions in acreage, according to

the UN data, occurred in the mid- and late 1990s, before asparagus production took off. The Peruvian government also eradicated tens of thousands of hectares in the 2010s.

From asparagus to seed

Whether it helped stop cocaine trafficking or not, Dayton residents know the plant isn't coming back.

The white brick outline of a larger-than-life Jolly Green Giant still sits on a hillside above town, well-maintained now after some years in disrepair.

"My husband says, 'Take it down, they're not here anymore.' I say, 'We're still the Valley of the Jolly Green Giant,'" Dickinson said.

The cannery was the largest private employer in Dayton at the time of its closure. But, Dickinson said, most of the jobs lost were people near retirement age. Seneca kept 10 workers on to work processing seeds, a business still going strong in the old Green Giant location.

Dayton's culture during harvest and packing season changed right away. Dayton children used to look forward to seeing their friends, the children of migrant workers, in class each spring.

"It was kind of a domino effect," said Brad McMasters, who was a third-grade student teacher when the plant closed, and now does economic development work for the Port. The laundromat closed, and a few bars shut down.

The workers often gathered in public spaces, sitting on downtown benches and socializing. Hearing Spanish on the street was common. Butler, the Dayton Historic Depot board member, said that sense of community was missing after the closure.

"I just felt like the fabric of Dayton was thinner," Butler said. Some families, like Ramos', stayed in the area, but many left for the Tri-Cites or other asparagus areas.

The economic impact of the closure would have hit harder, but wind power was booming just as Seneca moved asparagus to Peru. PacifiCorp began building

> "We are not going to dry up and blow away like a lot of farm towns."
>
> — *Jennie Dickinson*

the Marengo Wind Farm the same year, bringing in new construction jobs and some permanent jobs maintaining the turbines. A second farm, Hopkins Ridge, went in the following year, and a third came soon after.

Without those, "I can't even imagine what would have happened to us," Dickinson said.

Seneca has been expanding its seed processing operations. Plant manager Chris Shires said it employs about 50 people, half of whom are full time and half of whom work about 10 months a year. In the past six months, they've tripled their volume and now process 30 million pounds of pea, garbanzo and wheat seeds per year for three companies.

Because of that expansion, they're now using the full space once occupied by the asparagus cannery.

Washington's asparagus canning industry won't come back, something Schreiber said he's still bitter about. He's worked to reinvent Washington asparagus as a fresh crop, but said hundreds of people lost money when the plants shut down: farmers who plowed under fields, businesses who sold groceries and gas to migrant workers, families that relied on the income from plant workers.

"It's been a rough, gut-wrenching era," he said.

Dunlap retired from Seneca in 2002 and has since been active in the Blue Mountain Heritage Society, which recently restored a one-room schoolhouse from the county's early days and moved it into downtown Dayton. He sits on the board and did much of the painting to bring the old classroom back to life.

For Dickinson, the loss of lifelong company workers like Dunlap will be the true loss to Dayton. Wind farms provide good jobs, but the young people who take them often move up in the energy company and leave for a bigger city. Asparagus gave Dayton a supply of company men who retired, stayed in town and can give back now with community service.

But between tax revenue from wind farms, a budding local food movement and the town's proximity to a small ski area, hiking and agrotourism, Dayton isn't in danger of becoming a ghost town.

"We're just not going to dry up and blow away like a lot of farm towns," Dickinson said.

BLUEBERRIES

Blueberry production has ramped up across Washington during the past 10 years, propelling the state to the forefront of the U.S. industry — so far in front, in fact, that the Evergreen State now produces more organic blueberries than the rest of the country combined. Through that growth, the entire industry has been catapulted through a period of dynamic change as new processes and technologies come online.

FARMERS GO INTO THE BLUE

Washington is tops in the country in blueberry production

Story by Adriana Janovich, photos by Jesse Tinsley

THE SPOKESMAN-REVIEW

Janice Baker needed another bucket.

She was kneeling on the grass between rows at the end of the season, but she was mighty impressed with the size of the organic fruit still hanging on. "That is a big blueberry!" she exclaimed, holding up a specimen nearly the size of nickel.

"This," she said, "is good picking."

Blueberry production has ramped up across Washington during the past 10 years, including in Eastern Washington, where blueberries traditionally weren't grown until relatively recently.

Washington now ranks No. 1 in the country for overall blueberry production. In fact, Washington produces more organic blueberries than the rest of the states combined, according to Alan Schreiber, executive director of the Washington Blueberry Commission in Eltopia, north of Pasco.

"People historically liked blueberries because they tasted so good," Schreiber said. "But there were some studies done, and we saw growth across the board. The health effects of blueberries really stimulated consumption and so the demand went up, the price went up and growers started planting."

That demand kept increasing. And farmers in Washington, Schreiber said, "planted a lot of blueberries."

Gleaning the crop

In late August, when most of the rows were already harvested, Baker, 70, of Chattaroy, and two friends were enjoying "a girls' day of picking" at Willow Wind Farms, situated northwest of Spokane. Signs had directed them to rows 101–103, where they had been picking — and bantering back and forth between blueberry bushes — for not quite two hours.

"I'm going to be stiff and sore," said Baker, as she starting to fill a second pail. "My husband better enjoy this effort."

She was planning to bake him a pie.

While Baker was pleased with her two pails — one brimming, one just beginning — her haul was just a blip in the season's blueberry harvest at Willow Wind.

"We're a production farm," said blueberry grower Steve Walser, who provides U-pickers with buckets and relies on the honor system to get paid for the fruit. Guests weigh their own and place payment in a drop box. "It's very low-maintenance. I really only did U-pick because I want local people to be involved with the farm."

Blueberries from Willow Wind get shipped throughout the country. Walser is one of the local leaders in Eastern Washington's burgeoning organic blueberry industry, which is — along with conventional, or nonorganic, blueberries — in the midst of a dramatic period of growth and change.

Last year, Washington's total harvest came in at 120 million pounds, or six times what it was 10 years ago, Schreiber said. It's projected to weigh in at about 132 million pounds this year. And next year — assuming normal pollination

and no drought — Schreiber projects the state's blueberry harvest could reach 145 million pounds.

Washington became the national leader in blueberry production in 2015, when it surpassed Georgia — which actually produces more blueberries these days than its famous peaches. Behind Washington and Georgia in blueberry production are Michigan and Oregon.

In all, there are about 18,000 acres of blueberries in Washington. Of that, about 5,000 acres are in Eastern Washington, which now produces about 40 percent of this state's blueberry crop. "Eastern Washington has some of the largest blueberry growers in the world — all the way down to people who farm just a few rows of blueberries," Schreiber said.

Whatcom County on the west side still produces more than any other county in the state, with at least 7,000 acres of blueberries — a record number — twice as much as it grew in 2010. A third of those plants are 4 years old or younger.

Statewide, there's significant new production from young fields. And Washington will continue to experience that growth. Last year, at least 1,000 new acres of blueberries were planted in this state.

The push to grow more blueberries in Washington, particularly in Eastern Washington, started about 10 years ago. Before then, most of the blueberries grown in Washington were grown in Western Washington and were conventional. Now, organic blueberries make up about a

> " The health of blueberries really stimulated consumption and so the demand went up, the price went up and growers started planting. "
>
> *— Alan Schreiber*

OPPOSITE: Blueberry farmer Steve Walser holds a handful of berries at his farm. He says that blueberries are a good bet, once established, in Eastern Washington because there are fewer diseases and pests in this part of the state.

quarter of the total crop, Schreiber said.

Not only is organic and conventional blueberry production on the rise in Washington, it's also up worldwide — by 40 percent from 2012 to 2016, according to the U.S. Highbush Blueberry Council.

Consumption soaring

Popping plump, juicy, bush-ripe blueberries right into your mouth is one of the simplest and most sublime satisfactions of summer. But consumers are enjoying them much more than just as a fresh summertime snack. According to the U.S. Highbush Blueberry Council, blueberry consumption in America grew by a whopping 599 percent in the 20-year period from 1994 to 2014. And, as Schreiber noted, that demand continues to increase.

Industry experts, including him, credit recent studies that show berries are a good source of natural antioxidants for the boost in demand and production. Often referred to as a "superfood," blueberries are rich in vitamin C, manganese and more.

Plus, they taste good.

Gently sweet with just a whisper of tartness, blueberries can be used in both sweet and savory dishes. Tuck them into muffins, tarts, pies and other baked goods. Or, add them to pancakes, smoothies, salads, sauces, syrups, ice pops or ice cream. Use them to top yogurt or oatmeal or roast. Make them into jam.

Walser's favorite way to eat them: plucking them right off the bush and popping them in his mouth. During blueberry season, he walks through his rows, eating blueberries daily right off the bushes. It's a form of quality control.

"I love growing blueberries," he said. "I have grown everything there is to grow — in the Northwest, that is. And they're a challenge. Not everyone can do them."

But, "They're so rewarding."

'The economics of it'

Walser, whose blueberries are sold under the Naturipe label, first planted blueberries in 2009. "I saw the economics of it," he said, noting blueberries, especially organic blueberries like the ones he grows not far from the southwestern shores of Long Lake near Ford, can be a lucrative crop — particularly later in the season when blueberries fetch a higher price.

He started with 15 acres. Today, he grows nine varieties on about 33 acres and wants to expand — to some 100 to 150 acres of blueberries.

"This was my retirement project," he said, noting he was

A gallon of blueberries is evidence of a successful day at the U-Pick of Willow Wind Farm north of Reardan.

"relatively late" to the blueberry game. "I wish I had started 10 or 15 years before."

Inspired by the back-to-the-land movement of the mid-1960s and '70s, Walser began farming some 40 years ago. He bought this farm about five years after he got started, adding onto the acreage as he could. He grew potatoes back then. And he still grows other crops: hay, cherries, peaches, apricots, raspberries and, under the auspices of another business called Buddy Boy Farm, cannabis.

Blueberries aren't as lucrative as marijuana. But, Walser said, "The blueberries are making more money than the hay right now. The price escalates this time of year." Growers, he said, "are trying to get into that late market. It's where the money is. They'll play around with everything" — planting new varieties and test rows, for example — "so they can get there."

On the low end, organic blueberries fetch about $2.50 per pound to as much as $8 or $9 per pound for the farmer, he said. Nonorganic might top out at around $4.50 per pound, he said.

They're all harvested by hand.

And that's one of the challenges for the industry, Schreiber said. When it comes to labor, he said simply, "We do not have enough."

Of the farmworkers the blueberry industry does have, legal status can also be a concern. Based on a national study, Mike Gempler, executive director of the Washington Growers League, estimates about half of Washington farmworkers are undocumented — although, for some come crops, that percentage could be even higher.

Walser said he's lucky; he usually doesn't have trouble finding farmworkers for blueberry harvest. Most come from Spokane. Eight to 10 members of his crew return year after year.

Blueberry harvesters are paid by how much they pick. At the very least, they make minimum wage, which in Washington is $11, one of the highest in the country. In addition to a shortage of labor, the cost of labor is also a concern, Schreiber said.

Walser pays pickers 55 cents per pound, plus a bonus at the end of the season if they stay on through the end. Work is five days a week for about two months. Expert pickers can make around $250 per day, arriving as early as 5 a.m. to harvest during the cooler morning hours and quitting for the day around 1 p.m.

Grass grows between rows to keep the dust down and off the berries as well as maintain moisture. From here, berries go straight to cold storage, where they're cooled to 31 or 32 degrees.

In all the varieties Walser grows, "The differences are

Steve Walser walks his park-like blueberry field at his farm north of Reardan, Wash. "I just love coming down here, walking the field and eating blueberries," he said. Most of the bushes are done bearing by this time, but there are a few here and there.

really subtle."

Unlike with apples, however, most consumers don't really seem too concerned about blueberry varieties. Other than a few direct-market exceptions, such as farmers markets and sometimes U-pickers, consumers generally just want typical blueberries. Few varieties are labeled in supermarkets. So growers like Walser can select varieties to extend their season and offer better berries to wholesale firms, packing sheds or retailers.

This year, Walser's favorite is Blue Crop, a hardy, flavorful variety. He also likes Liberty blueberries "because they're so sweet." Draper is also "a really good variety. It's not a very big bush, and it gets loaded with berries." It used to be his favorite.

Duke ripens midseason. And those berries, Walser said, seem to "hang on the bush forever. They get big. They're

forgiving. They just sit there, getting sweeter."

Four 'vibrant' sectors

Production in Washington is made up of four sectors: organic fresh, organic processed, conventional fresh and conventional processed. "All four of those are very vibrant industries in Washington," Schreiber said.

That's partially because the blueberry plants here are some of the highest-yielding in the world, Schreiber said, noting they provide some 20,000 to 25,000 pounds per acre at maturity, even the organic fields.

Washington's also particularly well-suited for blueberry production because it enjoys a wide temporal range for harvest. "We have the climate," Schreiber said. "We also have a five-month picking window. No other state has that. Eastern Washington is early. Northwest Washington is late.

We start picking the first week of June and we go until the middle of October."

Washington is also home to some of the latest plantings in the country as well as the best varieties, technologies and post-harvest handling facilities, Schreiber said.

In Eastern Washington, "We don't have the pest pressure that they have in a lot of places," he said. "It's easy to grow organic berries here. As a result, we grow as many organic blueberries here in Washington than the rest of the country combined."

Last year, however, the industry didn't have the capacity to fresh-pack or process the entire crop it produced. In fact, Schreiber estimates that at least 40 percent of Washington's blueberry crop is packed or processed out of state. Oregon and British Columbia are primary destinations. But more than 2 million pounds each also go to Idaho and California,

BLUEBERRY GROWTH STAGES

Blueberries grow on bushes that range from 5 to 9 feet tall. The graphic shows stages in the fruit's life cycle.

① FLOWER BUD

In the spring the previously dormant flower buds swell and the outer buds begin to separate.

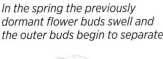

② FLOWER: EARLY PINK BUD

Pink-hued flowers are visible and separating. The petals are still closed. The flowers will open and become white tubes (corollas).

③ FRUIT: EARLY GREEN

The corollas fall off revealing small, green fruit. The fruit at this stage may be pea-size or larger.

④ FRUIT: 25 PERCENT BLUE

25 percent of the fruit is ripe. The first hand-harvest of the blueberries may occur at this stage.

⑤ FRUIT: 75 PERCENT BLUE

Blueberries are harvested several times as they ripen with later picking done by a machine that shakes the fruit from the bush.

Sources: Pacific Northwest Extension; Michigan State University Extension

MOLLY QUINN/THE SPOKESMAN-REVIEW

Schreiber said.

Washington's blueberry industry "is leaving a lot of income on the table" by sending fruit out of state for packing and processing, he said.

Whatcom, Snohomish and Skagit counties on the west side, and Benton and Franklin counties in Eastern Washington are the state's top blueberry-growing areas. In northwest Washington, Schreiber said, there's a need for increased fresh-pack capacity. And in Eastern Washington, he said, there's a need for increased freezing capacity. "My No. 1 concern is: How do we manage an industry that is rapidly moving to producing 200 million pounds of fruit?"

Exports, competition

Schreiber wants to expand Washington's blueberry exports — particularly to the Pacific Rim, including South Korea, India and Australia. Few blueberry growing regions are better situated for exports to that part of the world than Washington is, he said.

Imports are a growing concern, particularly from Peru, which can produce blueberries year-round and where production costs less.

There are challenges on the homefront, too. One is whether — or, rather, when — supply is going to outstrip demand.

Then, there are pests, such as spotted wing drosophila — small flies with red eyes that lay eggs in berries and stone fruit. Because of bugs and disease, it's difficult to grow organic berries in Western Washington.

Eastern Washington, on the other hand, is almost an ideal place to grow blueberries, including organic blueberries. It is, for the most part, disease-free and pest-free.

"Here in Eastern Washington, we don't have that many challenges," Schreiber said. "Our issues would be getting enough people to pick blueberries and the high cost of labor."

Another challenge is the soil itself. Blueberries, "are picky about that pH. They like low pH, really acidic soil. We start a year in advance prepping the fields," Walser said, noting two years would be even better. "We have to really build the soil."

The process involves adding compost, manure, sawdust, sulfur and rock phosphate to the soil well before planting. But that investment pays off. Blueberry plants, Walser said, "don't really decline as long as you treat them well — and they don't get some disease."

So far, disease hasn't been a major concern for blueberry growers on the east side of the state. And Walser gives great care to his crop. He checks on them daily during blueberry season.

"I come down here every day and eat blueberries," he said. "They're all good. There are no bad ones."

OPPOSITE: Blueberry farmer Steve Walser talks about growing blueberries in park-like fields at his farm. He raises only certified organic fruit on his farm, which also includes a marijuana operation.

CATTLE

No trade, perhaps, is as emblematic to the American West as the cattle ranch. Even today, family ranches stretch across a wide swath of America, from Central and Eastern Washington to the deserts of the Southwest. But the sector is changing, its practitioners aging and in competition with new, global factors — international price fluctuations, trade wars and a drier, hotter climate.

THE BUSINESS OF BEEF

Ranchers wrangle a living history off Eastern Washington scablands

Story by Thomas Clouse, photos by Tyler Tjomsland

THE SPOKESMAN-REVIEW

LAMONT, Wash. — Tucked within miles of barbed-wire fences and basalt columns southwest of Spokane reside what's left of the American West: Ranchers who scratch out a living from hard work and prairie grass.

Henry and Linda Harder live in a place where history flows as full as the swollen creek that feeds emerald-green grass, wild flowers and songbirds.

"It's a good place to be," Henry Harder, 52, said as he watched his herd of Hereford cows and their calves.

The Harders ride the tail end of an industry full of aging Washington ranchers who rely on beef prices that can fluctuate because of everything from droughts in the Midwest to threats of a trade war in China. While the industry is dominated by huge commercial operations, a few small ranchers like the Harders remain.

They live a history started by Henry's great-grandparents, Hans and Dora Harder, who came to these grasslands in 1881 from Germany. They settled near Kahlotus, Washington, where they raised sheep and sold horses to the Palouse Indians to make ends meet.

The remnants of their ax-hewn, split-rail cedar corral, built in 1896, survive at the old homestead.

The main window of the ranch home outside of Lamont reveals the same view that Lt. James Alden chalked in 1859 that he later memorialized into a painting. Alden, who would eventually become a U.S. Navy admiral, stood on the same hill 159 years ago as part of an inland expedition for the U.S. Coast Survey.

Behind the home is the field of honor where ranch trucks, former military vehicles and tractors of past, present and

---

"maybe someday" get equal billing.

The mechanical hulks bake in the sun next to a tin-roofed barn that is losing its long battle with thunderstorms and blizzards. Inside hang leather saddle bags and fence posts stamped "U.S." — as in U.S. Cavalry.

"You can see the Blue Mountains on a clear day," Henry Harder said. "I don't know what I would do if I couldn't live here."

Big get bigger

Some 8 miles past the bend in the road outside of Lamont, which counts its population with tally marks on the city sign, is Harder's Hangout.

Along the gravel road out of town sit abandoned foundations, shelter belts of trees used to block the wind and flat spots that once marked homesteads.

The road passes the saloon-turned-school house that hasn't hosted a math lesson for decades. The holes in its interior plaster walls now make homes for barn swallows and western kingbirds.

As the farmers left the land, through death, bankruptcy or a neighbor's offer, the remaining ranches grew. That is a national trend that continues today, said Sarah Ryan, the executive vice president of the 1,200-member Washington Cattleman's Association.

"It's really challenging in Washington ... to get started in ranching," she said. "If you don't have family, it's tough. You might have someone willing to let you run their place and

get ownership, but how do you get financing?"

Even if a descendant has the family land handed down, he or she may have to downsize just to pay off the inheritance tax, she said.

"It feels like it comes at you from every direction in agriculture," Ryan said. "At the same time, it's the greatest lifestyle. What's more rewarding than the success of raising an animal and producing something that is safe, wholesome and nutritious?"

Henry Harder's father, Carl Harder, had to sell his 180 cows in 1985 as he faced the financial challenges of kids in college, high interest rates and too much debt.

"I always dreamed of owning my own cows," Henry Harder said. "You'll never get rich at it, but you'll have a pretty good life."

Henry and Linda married in 1993 and moved to the current ranch house. Three years later, they cashed out the $10,000 they had socked away for retirement and bought their first 10 cows.

The Harder herd now includes 147 cows, 38 heifers, 143 calves and seven bulls.

"Every cow here today was born here. I'm proud of that," Linda Harder said. "You improve your herd by introducing new genetics. And you can't build your good genetics if you don't buy good bulls."

The Harders are trying to grow their herd, which Henry said must have 200 head just to make the operation pencil out. They expected to get about $942.50 for a 650-pound

> "At the same time, it's the greatest lifestyle. What's more rewarding than the success of raising an animal and producing something that is safe, wholesome and nutritious?"
>
> — *Sarah Ryan*

steer at current prices.

"We were getting ($1,300 to $1,430 for the same steer) six years ago," Linda said. "That was wonderful. But, it's very cyclical."

The Harders own or lease about 3,000 acres to support their herd, which often must be moved to prevent overgrazing in an area where grass often turns brown by mid-June. They also run cattle on 2,000 acres owned by an uncle.

"If you count all of the aunts and uncles, we run 12,000 to 13,000 acres," Henry Harder said. "There is a slug of us Harders."

He will never forget what his grandfather, Harry Harder, told his dad in 1964 just before he died. "He told my dad, 'It will be harder to keep it than it was for me to put it together.'"

Ranch life

A rancher must be a mechanic, welder, veterinarian and homesteader all wrapped into one.

"If you said there is nothing to do, you've never left the house or you are lying," Henry Harder said. "There is always something you need to do."

The family uses a homemade ATV trailer, which has recycled aluminum hazard signs for walls and an old iron hay spike welded onto an axle to allow ranch hands to roll out the spools of barbed wire needed for fencing.

Asked how much time he dedicates to fencing, Harder replied: "Not enough."

Post-hole diggers mostly find rocks just below the soil's surface, so Harder's grandfather bought a jackhammer in the 1950s to bore holes into the basalt. "Fire can go through, and that post (in the jackhammered rock) will still be there," he said.

The family uses a 1982 Chevy flatbed to haul hay. It has a front bumper that got pulled outward when a young ranch hand failed to understand that you don't allow slack in the tow chain before you hit the brakes. Its left front blinker light hangs by its wires. But it runs, and that's good enough.

"It's a low-budget operation," Harder said.

The family found 13 rattlesnakes in the front yard last summer. Linda Harder handles the ranch's bookwork and her favorite thing in all the world is Amazon, followed by the UPS driver who delivers what she needs.

"Before that, you had to go to Spokane to try to find what you were looking for," she said. "And nothing ever breaks down until nothing is open."

Even something as simple as phone service was an adventure at the ranch. The remnants of the old phone line sit slack on the aging poles all the way from the Harders' turnoff to Lamont.

In 1996, the family buried 5½ miles of cable, which the phone company donated as long as the Harders installed it. Prior to that, Henry had to check the phone line by horseback whenever they lost service.

He would ride out, shimmy up the pole with climbing spikes on his boots and put alligator clips on the phone line. "If you had a dial tone, you knew it's good to town and the problem was behind you," he said.

When he couldn't find the problem, he kept searching. Each of the 26 miles of line had 16 poles to check.

"In the old days, I'd have to do that four or five times a year," Harder said. "I wouldn't trade those memories for nothing."

The cattle drive

Just before Mother's Day, the family started gathering forces for the annual cattle drive and branding.

The crew included sheep rancher and veterinarian Jill Swannack and Mike and Stephanie Lewis, of Graham, Washington. Mike Lewis said he has worked 29 years for Boeing and 26 years as a farrier, a specialist who trims and shoes horses.

"One of my clients is a nephew. (The Harders) said they needed help," Lewis said. "We came out and helped them a couple years ago. They can't get rid of us now. We love 'em."

Among the six riders was 20-year-old Thailor McQuistion, Linda Harder's step-granddaughter, who will work at the ranch as a hand this summer.

"I've been helping for eight years," McQuistion said. "I'm probably not going to make a career out of this, but whenever I get the chance, I come down and help."

The crew hauled the horses and riders in a trailer over to one of the family pastures and began the drive that would end back at the ranch.

Linda rode a newly acquired mare, Kit Kat. Within minutes, the horse had bucked Linda off, and Henry raced over in a truck to check on her.

"I had a notion yesterday," she said. "As soon as I felt her about to buck, I bailed."

Linda landed on her shoulder and back, and the fall bent her glasses. She would later have to go to town to get treated for a mild concussion.

"Congratulations. You bought a horse," Linda said as she passed the reins of the skittish horse to Henry.

Henry and Kit Kat then trotted off to catch up with the drive. "He's a lot bigger to buck off," Linda said of her husband.

As the line of horses advanced, the cows started to bawl, calling to their calves. They nervously looked about and began to bunch up into a herd.

The cows approached the fence along the road, prompting one of the Harders' new Black Angus bulls to stick his swollen neck over the fence. The parade of bawling cows passed by as the bull watched with long strings of saliva swinging down from his mouth.

Eventually, the riders, including the Harders' 24-year-old son, Harry, popped over the basalt ridges and ravines and herded the cows toward an open gate.

Among them was Henry Harder on Kit Kat.

"He's happy being out there," Linda said as she watched. "We have a heckuva time finding good horses."

Just a minute later, Kit Kat went one way and Henry went the other. The saddle slipped, and Henry bailed off a just a few feet off the ground and hit with a thud. Choice words were spoken. Kit Kat scampered over the hill as she kicked at the empty saddle riding on her side.

Despite the horse drama, the riders got the bawling cattle pushed to an open gate, where they followed the loaded hay truck down the road to the corral.

"You are always learning," Harder said. "Herding calves is like herding field mice: They go everywhere."

Within a few minutes, the cows and calves were confined to the corral near the ranch.

Henry and Linda then trucked out enough food to feed a small army.

"Today was, well, I don't know what it was," Henry Harder said. "It's never pretty."

"Are the cows in the corral?" Linda shot back.

"There's the right way and there's the Harder way," Henry replied. "Just when you think you have everything figured out, that's when it jumps up and bites you."

Chinese middle class could be boon for Washington ranchers

THE SPOKESMAN-REVIEW

The prices that small-operation ranchers in Washington get for their cattle is tied to the global economy, making it about as hard to predict as the prairie rain.

Dick Coon, 66, ranches the ground his grandfather purchased just after World War II about 6 miles from Benge, Washington. He's been part of his family's 11,000-acre ranch since 1973.

"I'd say we are at the center of everything," Coon said of his ranch. "It's about equal distance to the Tri-Cities, Lewiston, Moscow, Spokane and Moses Lake."

Coon recently returned from a meeting where he was elected to serve on the executive committee for the National Cattlemen's Beef Association. He represents the region that includes Washington, Idaho, Montana, Colorado, Wyoming and Alaska. It coordinates efforts with the 1,200-member Washington Cattlemen's Association.

"I'm getting a national perspective on our business that I didn't have before," he said.

Part of the job of the national board is to coordinate advertising for the industry. The group is now trying to tailor a message that once included actor Sam Elliott announcing in the early 1990s: "Beef. It's what's for Dinner." The new campaign must now resonate with millennials.

"We are trying to figure out how to market to those consumers," Coon said.

But the prices that ranchers, including Coon and his family, receive at the stockyards largely rely on regional and international influences, he said.

"Three or four years ago, we had a big spike in cattle prices," he said. "It caught a lot of people by surprise. Our export demand was high and our own demand was high. We had a drought in the Midwest and millions of cattle were taken out of production."

But many of those dynamics have changed, and prices have fallen. Now ranchers are eagerly waiting to see how a brewing trade war with China plays out.

"We are selling lots of beef to Taiwan, South Korea and Japan," Coon said. "We just got into China last year. That had us excited. China's middle class is larger than the whole population of the U.S."

One of the first things to change after an economy grows is that the middle class population starts to improve its diet, he said.

"Hopefully, we'll get more beef in there," he said of China. "But that's been pushed back by this tariff hiccup."

The key for all ranchers, from small ranchers like the Coons, who have 400 cows between two herds, to large commercial operations, is that they must keep producing something the consumer wants, he said.

"If I can't keep the consumer happy and produce something that is reliably tender ... then I haven't done my job," Coons said. "That gives me the right to wear a big hat and boots and live a great lifestyle."

CATTLE ON FEED

Numbers for 1,000 head of cattle for January 2015

1-25 26-251 252-2,551 Unreported

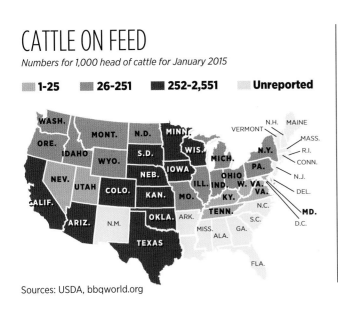

Sources: USDA, bbqworld.org

WASHINGTON BEEF CATTLE

Although falling steadily since 1984 the beef cow inventory in Washington has seen a slight increase in the past four years.

Scale in thousands

500
450
400
350
300
250
200
150

'80 '82 '84 '86 '88 '90 '92 '94 '96 '98 '00 '02 '04 '06 '08 '10 '12 '14 '16 '18

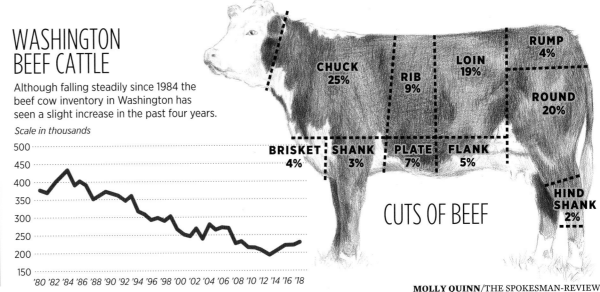

CHUCK 25%
RIB 9%
LOIN 19%
RUMP 4%
ROUND 20%
BRISKET 4%
SHANK 3%
PLATE 7%
FLANK 5%
HIND SHANK 2%

CUTS OF BEEF

MOLLY QUINN/THE SPOKESMAN-REVIEW

CHERRIES

Washington reigns over U.S. cherry production, generating more than twice the tonnage of sweet cherries than the next two leading states, Oregon and California, combined. Yet behind the numbers, uncertainty looms. Though only a third of the state's harvest finds its way onto international markets, exports account for nearly three quarters of the industry's value, and as the prospect of a trade war brews on the horizon, farmers look forward with some anxiety regarding the future of their crop.

KING OF CHERRIES

Tariffs are another risk for farmers who've made Washington the crop's top producer

Story by Thomas Clouse, photos by Tyler Tjomsland
THE SPOKESMAN-REVIEW

WENATCHEE — Convoys of headlights looked like glowworms in the predawn darkness Thursday morning as migrant workers coaxed aging vehicles up more than 1,500 feet of switchback roads to hilltop orchards above, one last great push in the harvest of the nation's largest cherry crop.

Parking in the dirt, the workers milled about, waiting for Michelle Gutzwiler to hand out the cards that would track how many boxes each picker would fill. The cards, workers, boxes and vehicles made up the last act in Gutzwiler's great annual gambit: that the previous eight months of work would pay off.

"Our expenses and equipment costs are over $100,000. Our bills are due in October," she said. "But we won't know how we did until we get paid in November. I can cry and beat on doors, but it doesn't come any faster."

Gutzwiler is just one of scores of cherry producers who make Washington the king of the succulent but temperamental fruit. Of the 61,000 acres under cherry cultivation in the Northwest, some 69 percent produce fruit in the Evergreen State.

Washington farmers produce more than double the tonnage of sweet cherries of the next two leading states, Oregon and California, combined. Derek Sandison, director of the state Department of Agriculture, said Washington cherries represent a half-billion-dollar industry, and are the No. 6 cash crop for the state.

However, of that amount, some $358 million came from exports, meaning about 72 percent of the overall revenue from cherries comes from the 35 percent of the crop sold on international markets. As a result, any tariffs or trade

disruptions pose an added economic risk that could end up hurting local farmers, Sandison said.

"Historically, one of the reasons we have been able to compete so well in export markets is because we have a good reputation for the quality of our cherries," he said.

But it's also a crop that can crash with a single wind event or hailstorm. Once farmers get their cherries to the finish line, their paychecks rely on a market rocked by trade wars over tariffs and other marketing decisions that are out of their control.

"In my mind, farmers take the biggest risk out of everyone who takes a piece of that pie. The warehouse, the marketers, the truck drivers and the shippers all get paid regardless. But we work all year to make this crop," Gutzwiler said. "They never work for an entire year and then lose it all."

Jorge's opportunity

Gutzwiler grew up in East Wenatchee with the goal of getting out of her hometown. She didn't make it far.

In 2000, she married Jake Gutzwiler, who works as a quality control manager at Stemilt, a fruit company that operates a warehouse in Wenatchee.

She stays home with their three children and runs the picking crews on the 23 acres they've planted, mostly with Sweetheart cherries, which are larger and mature later than their cousin, the more abundant Bing cherry.

While she's embraced the role of a farmer's wife, Gutzwiler said she's never fully learned to deal with the uncertainty.

"I'm married to a wonderful man. I knew that was part of the deal," she said. "On our wedding day, I said yes to the man and yes to the way of life."

Farming cherries includes pruning the trees in the winter, which Michelle is barred from doing. The work is supervised by Jake, who has a master's degree in horticulture from

Washington State University.

But the couple also must pay for fuel costs to operate wind machines that move cold air to prevent frost from killing cherry blossoms. They also must pay to spray insecticides to keep a host of bugs from eating what they hope to sell.

Add in the normal living costs, like paying for the home they purchased from father-in-law Norm Gutzwiler in Wenatchee Heights, and finances can cause some stress.

"There are so many years that you don't make any money. But it teaches them how to work," she said, referring to her three children. "That's why we have the orchard. They will be so much better off in the long run."

Growing up in the area, Gutzwiler said her father barred her from working in the orchards with men from out of the area whom she didn't know.

"I had friends in high school who went and picked in the orchards," she said. "But I haven't had a single kid (from Wenatchee) ask to pick."

Instead, each year, the family relies on temporary workers from Mexico. Many of them start the season picking cherries in California. They move to the Tri-Cities, where cherries mature faster, and then move north to Wenatchee for the late cherries and the beginning of apple season.

The Gutzwilers' best picker is Jorge Bacquez, 29, of Chiapas, Mexico. Last year, he made his personal best by picking seven 330-pound bins of cherries in one day. Paid $60 per bin, Bacquez picked five bins each on Thursday and Friday, which was by far the most of any picker.

"He's one of the best workers I've ever had," she said. "He's respectful. He's gentle on the tree. He's just good all the way around."

Bacquez said he's been coming to the United States for work since 2008. He started working in Pasco in May and came north for the later cherry season in Wenatchee. He will

NORTHWEST CHERRY EXPORTS

Here's where cherries from Washington, Oregon, Idaho, Utah and Montana were exported in 2017.

Number of 20-pound boxes

EUROPE
201,614

CANADA
2,720,915

CHINA
2,976,841

SOUTH KOREA
985,962

JAPAN
179,666

TAIWAN
852,826

HONG KONG
312,668

MEXICO, CENTRAL, SOUTH AMERICA, PUERTO RICO
276,168

EXPORT TOTAL
9,292,775

DOMESTIC TOTAL
17,139,419

OTHER FAR EAST
557,604

OTHER
18,925

GRAND TOTAL
26,432,194

AUSTRALIA
209,586

Source: Northwest Cherry Growers

EXPORT CROP HAS GREATER VALUE

Last year, Washington cherries brought in about $500 million in revenue. However, of that amount, some $358 million came from exports. That means about 72 percent of the overall revenue from cherries came from about 35 percent of the crop. As a result, any tariffs or trade disruptions pose an economic risk that could end up hurting local farmers, said Derek Sandison, director of the Washington State Department of Agriculture.

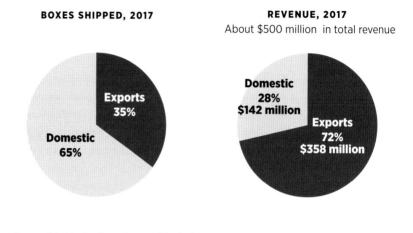

BOXES SHIPPED, 2017

Exports 35%

Domestic 65%

REVENUE, 2017
About $500 million in total revenue

Domestic 28% $142 million

Exports 72% $358 million

Source: Washington Department of Agriculture

MOLLY QUINN/THE SPOKESMAN-REVIEW

---

leave again for Mexico in October when the apple picking is done.

For the season, Bacquez earns $20,000 to $22,000, which he said he will use to support four other family members in Chiapas.

"I like to pick cherries," Bacquez said. "This, especially, is the best time of year to make a little more money. And the job is kind of easy. Picking apples is harder."

In the 10 years Bacquez has come to the Northwest, he said he's never seen anyone but migrant workers in the orchards.

"That's what I always ask myself, 'Why do they say we are stealing jobs when they don't want to do this kind of job?'" he said. In Mexico, "I didn't have a chance. That's the reason I had to come here."

But he fears changes in immigration law may prevent him from returning, making this summer the last with the Gutzwilers.

Tariff entanglements

Sandison, the state ag director, met in Wenatchee on July 3 with U.S. Sen. Maria Cantwell, D-Wash., to discuss the potential damage of a second round of tariffs by China in response to tariffs placed on aluminum and steel by President Donald Trump. The new Chinese tariffs came three days later.

"That really had a negative effect on the growers," he said. "It's the producers, the growers, who in the end get hurt."

China already had a 10 percent tariff on imports of U.S. cherries before the trade war kicked off. It added a 13 percent value-added tax this spring, then another 15 percent tariff, and later another 25 percent in response to the moves by Trump.

B.J. Thurlby is the president of Northwest Cherry Growers, which gets paid by producers to market the cherries to major retailers in the U.S. and abroad. He said the organization got its first cherries into China in 2002 and started direct flights to Shanghai in 2006.

"It took a few years to get it going. But it's really taken off," Thurlby said. "That's because the middle class in China has really taken off."

Last year, the trade organization that represents producers in Washington, Oregon, Montana, Idaho and Utah shipped 3 million boxes of cherries to China. This year that dropped to about 1.4 million boxes.

"It feels like we have been thrown under the bus four separate times since May," Thurlby said.

The Chinese government eventually lowered the overall tariff to 50 percent, but then forced its importers to pay the tariff up front. In turn, the Chinese importers required the American exporters to lower prices to cover the 50 percent tariff, Thurlby said.

That means cherry growers eventually will get about half what they would have made last year.

"We just know the returns are going to be a bit lower," Thurlby said. "But the prices this year have been pretty good. The domestic consumer has really taken to our fruit this year and we are grateful for it."

OPPOSITE: Jorge Bacquez raises an orchard ladder as the moon hangs above him while harvesting cherries on an early August morning at Jake and Michelle Gutzwiler's orchard in Wenatchee, Wash.

Jorge Bacquez, 29, of Chiapas, Mexico, is the fastest picker at Jake and Michelle Gutzwiler's orchard in Wenatchee, Wash. His personal best is seven 330-pound bins of cherries in one day.

Hot weather on the East Coast has helped farmers in Washington, he said. Thurlby explained that the association researches other items that American consumers purchase when they buy cherries. Some of the top items were hamburgers and buns.

"Cherries are the type of item they buy for a picnic or barbecue," he said. "The consumer is getting a great year.

They have great prices and great fruit."

Life of riches

Norm Gutzwiler, 71, rises each day before the sun illuminates the Wenatchee Valley.

He walks his black Lab, Max, along the Columbia River before he heads to the orchard to carry on a family legacy

that his grandparents started in 1902.

"It's almost my second love," Gutzwiler said of his cherries. "I've got my wife. I've got my hunting and fishing, and then I've got my orchard. It's been a great way to raise our family."

Gutzwiler, who along with Jake and Michelle farms a total of about 75 acres of cherries, began taking out the

Bing trees a few years ago and replacing them with Skeenas and Sweethearts, which are both later-maturing varieties.

"We like to leave them on the tree until they reach full maturity," he said. "We don't get excited about getting them off the tree like earlier people. We try to give the consumer that last great taste of cherries before they go to apples and pears."

Unlike apples, which can be preserved in cold storage and sold all year long, cherry growers must race to pick, process and place them on the shelf, where they only last about a week before they go soft.

"It's such a sweet, delicate product," he said.

But to start from scratch or to replace an orchard, the farmer must shell out about $40,000 an acre, said Gutzwiler, who earlier retired from his other job as a horticulturist.

"In the fourth year, you get a small amount of cherries to pay some of the debt back," he said. "By the seventh year, you are hoping the markets are good."

Farmers enjoyed a bumper crop in 2017. The conditions produced lots of cherries but the market was weak.

"Last year was probably my most disappointed year I've ever had," Gutzwiler said. "A lot of people went out of business last year. A lot of us just flat lost money. We did not get the money back that we put into growing the crop."

In 2017, some farmers received as little as 25 cents per pound. Earlier this year, the price had rebounded to about $1.25 per pound, he said.

"I can deal with Mother Nature. It's something I can't control," Gutzwiler said. "But when it's a market that we as an industry can control, that's disappointing. We should be able to move that crop and get a return back to the grower."

Michelle Gutzwiler said she was rooting through some of the items that Norm Gutzwiler "forgot" to move out when

he sold the house to the next generation. In the corner, she found some of his old books.

"We found the cherry returns for 1976 and 1977. They got the same price then as it is now," she said. "We'd be rolling in dough if we just made minimum wage."

Despite the weak market last year and trade war this year, Norm Gutzwiler said he'll continue to follow his family legacy.

"It's the life that we've chosen. You either enjoy it or you don't," he said. "I enjoy being outside. I enjoy watching the trees and the fruit. I enjoy my family and my neighbors. I'm very fortunate."

July-August

Other challenges

RAIN

May cause the fruit to crack as the fruit is getting set.

HAIL OR WINDSTORMS

Can damage or knock off the fruit.

HEAT

Temperatures over 100 degrees cause the cherries to soften.

MOLLY QUINN/THE SPOKESMAN-REVIEW

Racing the perishable cherry to market

PICKED FAST

The grower must hire dozens of workers to pick the crop in a matter of days.

Forty pickers may pick 10 to 12 tons of cherries each day.

COOLED DOWN

The fruit is transported from the orchard to cold storage. Crews put the cherries through a cold wash that drops the temperature in the fruit to 38 to 40 degrees.

COMPUTER SORTED

Cherries are sent through optical sorting lines, which grade the fruit quickly and accurately. Cameras send a signal to a computer, which prompts an air compressor to shoot a burst of air that pops out any individual cherry that has a problem.

CULLED CHERRIES *(a one-day snapshot)*

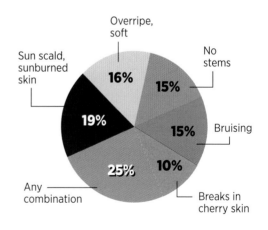

Overripe, soft 16%
No stems 15%
Bruising 15%
Breaks in cherry skin 10%
Any combination 25%
Sun scald, sunburned skin 19%

KEPT COLD FROM WAREHOUSE TO THE STORE

Cherries are loaded into refrigerated trucks and shipped to all corners of the United States. Some 35 percent of those cherries are trucked to Seattle where they are placed on refrigerated freighter airplanes and sent to everywhere from China to Australia.

CHERRIES LAST ABOUT A WEEK ON STORE SHELVES

Wherever the cherries end up, they last only about a week on the store shelf before they begin to lose their firmness.

CORN

After thousands of years' cultivation as a staple foodsource, the development of corn — and, for Americans in particular, sweet corn — has gone into overdrive with the modernization and industrialization of farming. In Washington state, one of the top three producers of sweet corn in the country, those trends will continue to shape local agriculture and the livelihoods of those who practice it.

AMAZING MAIZE

Columbia Basin's super sweet corn is a story of modern agriculture

Story by Eli Francovich, photos by Tyler Tjomsland

THE SPOKESMAN-REVIEW

QUINCY, Wash. — Russ Kehl tears an ear of corn from a field of thousands, shucks it and takes an enthusiastic bite.

It's part theater. He's acting for two journalists standing in his field outside of Quincy. But as he chews he examines the corn cob, and the acting stops.

Kehl is struck by the perfectness of this randomly picked ear of corn.

Even eaten raw, it's sweet. Each kernel perfectly formed. No signs of pest or disease. A uniform size with a tapering point. Built to factory specifications.

"This is good. Really good corn," Kehl said. "Honestly, this is really good."

It's no accident that the corn is so good.

The story of corn — sweet and field alike — is the story of modern agriculture. As humans have exerted increasing control over nature, we've manipulated the taste, texture and look of food. Bitter tastes are masked, or bred out. Sweeter vegetable variations are intentionally bred. More tender corn is grown. Per-acre yields increase.

During the last century sweet corn has been carefully bred for taste, size and uniformity. Modern super sweet varieties, which are planted throughout the Columbia Basin as a rotation crop, can be as much as 40 percent sugar.

In fact, traditional sweet corn, which was the norm just a generation ago, tastes downright bland in comparison. Those changes are only accelerating, driven in part by Americans' sweet tooth and in part by the demands of large food processors.

Corn, a food staple for thousands of years, illustrates these rapid changes and highlights the often-conflicting interests of taste, health and the competitive, sometimes cutthroat business of large-scale agriculture.

"What they used to call in the old days 'Golden Jubilee' was the best thing you could ever imagine," said Rick Ness, a third-generation farmer near Moses Lake. "And nowadays it's just a plain old corn."

Like most farmers, Ness plants sweeter and sweeter corn each year.

"The market is just headed that way," he said. "You know, you adapt to the market, or you lose."

Sweeter, softer, faster

For a number of genetic and economic reasons, corn has led the charge of changing fruits and vegetables.

Genetically, corn is a "highly variable species" and one that is "relatively easy to manipulate," said Bill Tracy, an agronomy professor at the University of Wisconsin, Madison.

"In the last 50 to 60 years now, I guess, sweet corn has really dramatically changed," Tracy said. "If you look at the plants you wouldn't think they are very different, but if you bit the ears you'd find them to be quite different."

Super sweet corn was only developed about 70 years ago. In the early 1950s, a University of Illinois botany professor named John Laughnan discovered that a certain gene in corn stored less starch but held four to 10 times more sugar. He wrote a paper based on his discovery and tried to market it.

Initially, the corn industry had little interest in Laughnan's discovery, Tracy said. Food processors considered it a "disruptive technology." But the new variety took off in Japan, historically one of the U.S. corn industry's biggest buyers. From there it slowly spread back to the United States.

Because the corn is sweeter, processors don't have to add sugar, which saves them money. And sweet corn stays fresh longer.

"Super sweets became very important in the processing industry," Tracy said. "It's because you don't have to add the sugar. Traditional corn, you added sugar to the cans because it really wasn't very sweet."

In addition to changing the taste of corn, researchers have learned to breed for uniform size and texture. Food processors require farmers to meet exacting specifications. Those specifications allow large plants to process the corn quickly and efficiently.

At National Frozen Food Corp.'s 60-acre processing facility near Moses Lake, efficiency is the name of the game. Inside the cavernous processing plant machines rattle away in a cacophony of mechanization, all working toward a single goal: preparing corn.

In the cavernous facility conveyor belts shunt corn from the trucks where they're unloaded through a cleaning and husking machine. From there cobs go to be either cut into kernels or packaged as full frozen cobs.

During peak harvest time the plant can process between 6 and 7 million pounds of corn a day, said Gary Ash, general manager of the plant. On average, an ear of corn weighs 1 pound, he said.

That corn will be blanched (a process where the corn is scalded for 90 seconds in boiling water and then plunged into cold water) and then flash-frozen. The cobbed corn, or individual pieces of corn, are packed into 1,500-pound totes and sold wholesale.

And while the machines are fast and efficient, they aren't intelligent. Corn that doesn't meet the factory's specific size requirements will slow or jam the machines, potentially costing the company and the farmer money.

"Time is money just like any other industry," said Kevin Moe, a seed representative with Syngenta, an international seed agrochemical business. "We're not making widgets, but we try our best to punch out widgets."

The widget factory

In a dusty, torn-up field about 15 minutes east of the Tri-Cities, scientists, farmers and manufactures are hoping to breed the newest variety of corn.

Several acres of corn test varieties rustle in the October wind. Crammed into an acre plot are about 200 varieties of super sweet corn. These varieties are being field-tested. Eventually one, or maybe two, will be approved by Syngenta to be grown in larger quantities.

"We're searching for that one variety out of hundreds, if not thousands, that will make it to commercial scale," Moe said.

The different varieties of corn used to be individually named — Early Sunglow, Sundance and Buttergold, for example.

Now, new varieties get a 10-digit number. As they advance through the various field tests, they'll lose numbers. The ones that make it to full production will be labeled with just four digits.

Moe walks through the field randomly selecting and shucking cobs of corn, snapping them in two and examining their different attributes.

Some have larger, thicker kernels. On others, perfectly straight lines of kernels run up and down the cob.

"Just take a bite of that," Moe said, gesturing toward a plump, golden cob of corn. "It's just pure candy how sweet it is."

That cob is a descendant of the super sweets developed in the 1950s. About a mile away is another patch of test corn. This is the traditional sweet corn. Compared to the new, super sweet varieties, that corn is bland and tasteless.

Moe believes that what is happening with corn — the sweeter taste, higher yields and more factory-friendly specifications — is what needs to happen to all commercially grown vegetables and fruits.

"If we can provide the same amount of food, or more food, on the same acres ... everybody in the world is better off," Moe said.

With decreasing amounts of viable farmland, increasing water scarcity and a growing world population, food supplies will be of the utmost importance, he said.

But there are downsides to the kind of drastic human manipulation that defines the corn industry and increasingly modern agriculture.

"Modern plant breeding has focused on yields almost to the exclusion of anything else," said Jed Fahey, a professor of medicine and public health at Johns Hopkins University. "To the extent that it has focused on taste, sweetness and sugar have been what they've focused on."

More produce but less nutritious

That single-minded focus on crop yields has reduced the nutrients of modern fruits and vegetables, said Donald Davis, a retired professor from the University of Texas, Austin.

In 2004, Davis published a landmark study indicating that fruits and vegetables were losing nutritional value as farming increasingly focused on yields.

Davis examined 43 vegetables and fruits. He compared the reported nutritional values of those crops from 1950 with the tested nutritional value of the same crops in 1999. In the study, he compared the crops individually and as a group in an effort to get an overall average.

Davis said he believes the "dominant cause" for reduced nutritional value is increased yields. Simply put, if a plant grows faster and larger it doesn't have time to absorb the same amounts of nutrients as a slower, smaller plant. The plant's nutritional value is "diluted," Davis said.

"They are looking for yield. They are looking for uniformity," Davis said of modern crop breeders. "But when you do that, you may lose other things."

As a child, Davis remembers buying broccoli at the store. Back then you could only buy small, bunched broccoli.

Since then, breeders have figured out ways to increase the head size. But, as broccoli head size increases, the plant's stems become hollow and "ugly," Davis said. Now, many large-headed broccoli sold at the store come with their stems removed.

"The larger the head, the lower mineral concentration," Davis said.

Since Davis' 2004 study, other studies have found similar results. Increased yields lead to decreased nutrients. And while the yields increase, the flavor of many vegetables decreases, studies have found.

"In general, the flavor of veggies have gone down over the years," Davis said. "Tomatoes are a pretty good example."

As tomatoes have gotten larger and sturdier, their flavor has decreased. This year scientists discovered some of the genes that control a tomato's taste. They hope to breed the flavor back into tomatoes while keeping the desirable size and durability.

And in the crops where flavor has increased, such as sweet corn, it tends to increase in narrow taste bands. Fruits and vegetables become sweeter.

"As far as of this breeding for sweetness, I think this is because Americans have a sweet tooth," Davis said.

In addition to reduced nutrients, carefully bred vegetables and fruit appear to lack another important element: a type of chemical linked to cancer prevention and the avoidance of other chronic diseases that plague Americans.

Reducing diversity

Jed Fahey worked in the biotechnology industry for 15 years. There he tried to improve plants' disease resistance through breeding and genetic manipulation. However, the shifting priorities of the biotechnology industry bothered him. So he quit.

"I got tired of it, frankly, and I came to Hopkins seeing that I might be able to realize my altruistic interest in

"As far as of this breeding for sweetness, I think this is because Americans have a sweet tooth."

— *Donald Davis*

feeding the world," he said. "In feeding the world better."

That's where he started researching a type of chemicals known as phytochemicals. Now, at Johns Hopkins University, Fahey is the director of the Lewis B. and Dorothy Cullman Chemoprotection Center. There, Fahey researches how nutrition can protect humans from chronic and degenerative diseases.

As part of that research Fahey studies phytochemicals.

Phytochemicals are a type of chemical produced in plants that wards off pests and diseases. When eaten they often taste bitter.

And they are linked to the prevention of cancer and

CORN PRIMER

On many irrigated Columbia Basin fields, farmers double-crop. They may plant peas in late winter or early spring and harvest the legumes in June. Corn is planted right afterward, taking advantage of the nitrogen peas have fixed in the soil. The corn is then grown for an autumn harvest.

POLLINATION

Pollination can begin as early as 45-50 days and is necessary to produce the corn kernel on the cob.

Tassels are the male reproductive portion of the corn plant and normally appear 2-3 days before silk emergence.

Silk is the female portion of the corn plant and is fertilized by pollen from the tassels once it starts emerging from the husk.

A tiny tassle starts to form sometime after two weeks.

About a week after planting.

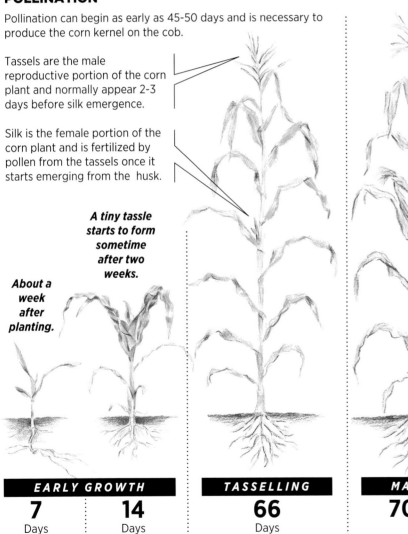

EARLY GROWTH	
7	**14**
Days	Days

TASSELLING
66
Days

MATURITY
70-100
Days

Sources: Seminis, Agricultural Statistics Service

HARVEST

Sweet corn will be ready for harvest about 18-21 days after the emergence of silks.

The silks on the ear should be brown and dry. When a thumbnail is pressed into a kernel, a milky liquid should emerge indicating the crop is ready for harvest.

Sweet corn must be harvested quickly at the proper stage because the sugars in kernels can convert to starch, making it less sweet and undesirable.

SWEET CORN COUNTIES

Washington is ranked No. 2 nationally for processed corn.

WASHINGTON

GRANT   ADAMS

FRANKLIN

BENTON

BY THE NUMBERS

Sweet corn production in 2016.

$104,366,000
Total sweet corn value

$91,580,000
Sweet corn processed market value

$12,786,000
Sweet corn fresh market value

93,500
Acres of sweet corn harvested

MOLLY QUINN/THE SPOKESMAN-REVIEW

other chronic diseases.

Research is conflicted on just how important these chemicals are. Unlike basic nutrients, phytochemicals are not required for human health, Fahey said. But they do have health benefits.

"The protective mechanism that phytochemicals induce in many people are real and important," Fahey said.

And just like the basic nutrients, modern agricultural breeding practices are slowly reducing the phytochemicals in fruits and vegetables.

"Indeed, the low amounts of bitter plant compounds in the current diet largely reflect the achievements of the agricultural and food industries," stated a review of literature published in the American Journal of Clinical Nutrition. "The debittering of plant foods has long been a major sensory concern for food science."

Humans are able to detect minute traces of bitterness in food. It's an evolved skill, one used to avoid eating poisoned or rotten foods. The food industry has developed numerous ways to either mask or remove these flavors.

"Through both the breeding selection for yield, and the intensive use of pesticides, phytochemical content has gone down," Fahey said.

Although Fahey is a phytochemical evangelist, at the end of the day his primary concern is much simpler: Humans should eat a varied diet, one rich in nutritious vegetables.

And that, he said, is the true downside of modern, scaled agriculture. The diversity normally present in an acre of corn, for instance, is being methodically replaced with carefully engineered, factory-ready widgets.

Better for everyone

Bill Tracy, the agronomy professor at the University of Wisconsin, Madison, disagrees with this assessment.

Sure, he said, humans have an unprecedented ability to control how vegetables and fruits grow. But he believes there are constraints on what will be done. While developing higher-yield crops certainly is important, he said, it's not the only thing breeders consider.

"There has been a major effort to really concentrate on quality," he said.

As an example, he cites sweet corn. In addition to tasting sweeter, "modern sweet corns are much more tender." And, he said, some studies indicate that modern sweet corn has

Marcelino Medina unloads a truck of sweet corn at National Frozen Foods, Moses Lake Facility. The plant can harvest up to 300 acres a day.

more protein than its ancestors.

"For every bite of a super sweet ear you take, you're getting less calories and more protein," he said.

As for the reduction of other nutrients in foods, and phytochemicals, Tracy said that's the exact point of having a balanced diet.

"You don't need to get every chemical from every food," he said. "That's why we talk about having a balanced diet."

And there is another, more practical argument for modern agriculture. The current mechanized and scaled agricultural system is the only thing that can simultaneously meet the needs of consumers, farmers and retailers, Kevin Moe said.

"It would be great if the American consumer, or the world consumer, ate another pound of sweet corn," Moe said. "It's better for them. Better for the grower. Better for the company. Everybody benefits."

'If you aren't getting bigger, you're getting out'

Russ Kehl started farming in 1992. That was a good year

to get into the business, he said. Farmers were struggling, selling or renting their land for cheap. He rented. Did well. His business grew. Now, his is one of the larger farms in the Columbia Basin area.

Yet he's not confident that he could replicate his success.

"It would be really hard to start farming today," he said.

That's because the size and sophistication of modern farming has only increased. With increased yields come increased harvests. Larger harvests demand more harvesting machinery, the people to run it and the infrastructure to store and transport the harvest.

That all costs. Those costs drive farmers to plant more acres. The cycle continues.

Kehl, a self-described aggressive farmer, is always looking to rent or buy neighboring land. To expand his own farming footprint.

"I just know every year it gets bigger," he said of farming. "If you aren't getting bigger, you're getting out."

Washington corn a 'hardy crop' that fills the gaps between potatoes and wheat

Story by Eli Francovich, photos by Tyler Tjomsland

THE SPOKESMAN-REVIEW

Washington isn't known for corn. But it should be.

Other crops, like apples, wheat and potatoes, dominate the state's industry, yet a drive through the irrigated heart of Washington reveals a farming landscape dotted with cornfields.

Unlike the corn grown in Iowa, Illinois, South Dakota and Minnesota, for example, Washington corn is a rotation crop — a useful planting in years the soil needs a break from potatoes or wheat.

In 2016, Washington farmers harvested about 93,000 acres of sweet corn and roughly 200,000 acres of field corn.

Washington, California, Florida, New York and Georgia grow the most sweet corn. Across all 50 states there are 28,000 farms growing sweet corn.

Russ Kehl, a farmer near Quincy, called sweet corn "low-risk" and consistent. He doesn't make much money off corn, but he doesn't lose money, either.

"I can put a budget line on sweet corn and I can hit it nine out of 10 times," he said.

An added benefit is that food processing companies — in Kehl's case, it's the National Frozen Food Corp. — harvest the crop. That saves Kehl time and equipment costs and allows him to invest and focus on his cash crop, potatoes.

The processors also choose what variety of corn the farmer plants.

"Sweet corn is a very good rotation for the growers down here," said Kevin Moe, a seed representative with Syngenta, an international seed agrochemical business.

National Frozen Foods has a plant in Moses Lake. That plant harvests corn in roughly a 20-mile radius around the plant, said Gary Ash, the plant manager.

"Corn is a pretty hardy crop. You rarely have a crop failure," Ash said. "Here in the Columbia Basin corn does really well. It's like growing in a greenhouse."

National Frozen Foods chooses the variety of corn to plant and harvests the corn. That's because they're engaged in a complicated game of musical chairs.

When corn is harvested is vital to how it tastes. If it's harvested too soon, it won't be tender and the taste won't be fully developed. Conversely, if it's harvested too late it will be too soft and won't store well.

In Washington, sweet corn harvest starts in the middle of July in the south of the Columbia Basin area. Harvest ends in the middle of October, Ash said. The picked corn goes to one of the three National Frozen Foods plants — in Moses Lake, Quincy and Chehalis. National Frozen Foods, and others, have to time the corn harvest down to the week. With different microclimates throughout the basin, this takes a coordinated effort.

During the peak harvesting times, National Frozen Foods picks about 300 acres a day, Ash said.

About 15 percent of National Frozen Foods' total production is exported, much of that going to Japan. Because there is no Washington state corn commodity commission, exactly how much Washington corn is sent overseas isn't clear.

Washington's key sweet corn counties are Adams, Benton, Franklin and Grant.

CRANBERRIES

For some 200 years after that first Thanksgiving, cranberries were picked in the marshes or swamps where they grew wild. It wasn't until 1816 that farmers in Massachusetts began cultivating them after discovering that adding sand to the soil improved the yield. But the harvest involved arduous stoop labor of picking by hand in soggy conditions.

BOGGED DOWN WITH BERRIES

Colorful crop is processed into juice, sauce, dried fruit

Story by Jim Camden, photos by Jesse Tinsley

THE SPOKESMAN-REVIEW

ILWACO, Wash. — Sloshing deliberately through water up to her knees, Guillermina Hernandez used one hand to swish floating cranberries away from the edge of the acre-and-a-half bog as she pulled the clearing boom around the perimeter with the other.

It is harvest time on CranMac Farm, and mist is rising from the bogs on a crisp October morning along the Long Beach peninsula, the cranberry capital of Washington state.

The boom, a growing line of 2-by-8 planks hooked together by flexible joints at 10-foot lengths, slowly snaked out in opposite directions, turning at the corners inside the rectangular bog to create a corral for the red berries that were beaten from their vines the previous afternoon.

After being connected end-to-end, the boom was drawn together in an ever-tightening polygon as Guillermina's husband, Juan, and others dragged V-shaped planks through the bog to force berries to the center.

When the boom seemed to have created an area rug of red sitting in the middle of a floor of cloudy brown water, a small motor sputtered to life and the panels of an elevator scooped berries out of the water and whooshed them into large wooden bins waiting on the backs of trucks.

The experienced six-person harvesting crew can gather and suck up an acre-and-a-half bog in a little over an hour. Malcom McPhail, who owns CranMac with his wife Ardell, said many of the crew have worked on the farm for years, including Juan — who has worked year-round on the farm for 17 years — and Guillermina, who are originally from Jalisco, Mexico.

OPPOSITE: A harvest crew shrinks a floating boom around a crop of floating cranberries in a bog at McPhail Family Farms in Ilwaco, Wash. The shrinking boom forces berries onto an elevator that empties them into bins on a truck.

FUN FACT NO. 1 ABOUT CRANBERRIES: *The second one will taste better than the first one you bite into.*

Fresh from the vine, cranberries have a taste somewhere between tart and bitter, which becomes clear when you bite into one. The second one will taste better because your taste buds have adapted.

They have little natural sugar and five times the acid of other commercial fruit crops like Red Delicious apples, peaches or grapes.

Most grade-school lessons about the first Thanksgiving mention cranberries being among the food items the Wampanoag Indians introduced to the Pilgrims after they settled in Plymouth. That may or may not be true; cranberries also grow in parts of England and the Netherlands, so the Pilgrims who had lived in both countries may have recognized them on their own.

But cranberries were plentiful in marshy areas of New England and Native Americans also used the red juice to dye blankets and clothing. It's unlikely the Wampanoags or the Pilgrims made cranberry sauce or cranberry jelly for that first Thanksgiving feast. Neither the natives nor the Europeans would have had the sugar to sweeten them up.

Native Americans mashed cranberries into dried deer meat to make pemmican, which could be stored for long periods and helped them through times when fresh food was in short supply. They also knew, without the need for FDA studies, the berries had medicinal qualities. High in

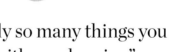

> "There's only so many things you can do with cranberries."
>
> — *Kim Patten, a WSU extension specialist*

vitamin C, the berries were eventually prized by ship crews to help prevent scurvy on long voyages.

For some 200 years after that first Thanksgiving, however, cranberries were picked in the marshes or swamps where they grew wild. It wasn't until 1816 that farmers in Massachusetts began cultivating them after discovering that adding sand to the soil improved the yield. But the harvest involved arduous stoop labor of picking by hand in soggy conditions.

FUN FACT NO. 2 ABOUT CRANBERRIES: *They float.*

Or at least the fresh ones do, before they are turned into juice, dried into Craisins or processed into sauce or jelly. If you cut one open, you can see the small air pockets inside.

That buoyancy is a key to harvesting a crop that is otherwise difficult to get from the field to the table. Even so, cranberry harvesting is labor intensive, which is just one of the challenges of growing one of America's oldest native crops.

They are also to subject to disease, insects, rot, and being trampled by elk and eaten by deer. Lately as a commodity they have seen fluctuations in consumer demand and erratic prices because of a glut of cranberries from Canada.

Cranberries are part of the same family of plants that includes heather, which they resemble at certain times of the year. They grow naturally in marshy or swampy areas on low vines. According to lore, German farmers thought the curving flowers on the vines looked like cranes, so they

CRANBERRY PRODUCTION

NUMBER OF BARRELS
Top U.S. states; estimates for 2017

A barrel weighs about 100 pounds

Massachusetts	2,200,000
New Jersey	590,000
Oregon	480,000
Washington	180,000
Wisconsin	5,600,000
United States	9,050,000

PRICE PER BARREL

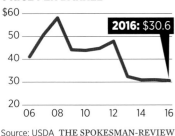

2016: $30.6

Source: USDA THE SPOKESMAN-REVIEW

A harvest crew works inside a floating boom filled with millions of floating cranberries in a bog at McPhail Family Farms in Ilwaco, Wash. The crew moves them toward an elevator that lifts them from the water to bins on the back of a truck.

called them "craneberrries." Or they came up with the name because cranes ate the berries. Or perhaps it was English or Dutch farmers — accounts vary.

Eventually, the first "e" was dropped.

By the mid-1800s, they were a major crop in New England and other parts of the northeastern United States. In the 1870s, a Massachusetts visitor to the southwest corner of Washington Territory noticed the region also had wild cranberries growing in land very similar to conditions back home, according to the history prepared by the state Cranberry Museum in Long Beach.

Land was cheap in the territory. For as little as $1 an acre, a syndicate bought up 1,600 acres and planted cranberry bogs on the long, skinny peninsula that stretches up from Cape Disappointment to separate the Pacific Ocean from Willapa Bay.

Washington's cranberry industry grew, but not without its problems. The plants imported from the East had new pests. Washington was a continent's width away from the main population centers where demand for the berries was highest. Enterprising growers tried different ways to pull berries from the vines, which included large wooden scoops with long spikes wielded by pickers.

A boom in the 1910s was followed by a bust in the 1920s that caused most Washington farmers to abandon the crop. To help the beleaguered industry, the Agriculture School at Washington State College sent a young undergraduate to Long Beach to look for ways to improve the harvest.

After J.D. Crowley graduated, he returned to Long Beach to set up the college's Cranberry Research Station, where for 30 years he worked on ways to beat pests, frost and other local problems. One change many peninsula farmers made was to switch to a wet harvest, flooding the bogs where the vines grow when the berries have ripened to a marketable red, then driving through the water with small tractors pulling or pushing rotary beaters that churn the water like the paddle wheel on a Mississippi River boat.

Knocked off the vines by the paddle blades, the berries float to the top of the water. Wet harvest is used for cranberries that are turned into dried fruit like Craisins, juice and canned jelly, but not for fresh ones sold in the supermarket produce section. Those are picked by small combines not much bigger than a lawnmower.

FUN FACT NO. 3 ABOUT CRANBERRIES: *Washington is the fifth-largest state for production. But it only grows about 2 percent of the total crop.*

Malcolm McPhail has been in agriculture all his life, but not always in cranberries.

Raised on a homestead cattle ranch that grew some grains, he was an area agronomist with a doctorate in soils and plant nutrition in Western Washington when he and wife Ardell "got enamored" with the idea of having their own farm. They considered vegetable farming in the Chehalis area where they lived, but didn't like the fact those farmers depended on processors for the harvesting. They looked at cranberry farming.

"You can do almost all of the stuff yourself," he said. "Everybody does their own delivery."

The berries are trucked in large wooden bins to a nearby holding facility where they are tested for color, firmness and rot. That facility sends larger truckloads up to the Ocean Spray processing plant in Markham, Wash., near Aberdeen.

The McPhails bought their first farm in 1981, bought a neighbor's farm the next year and slowly added to their holdings over the next 35 years. CranMac Farms, which Malcolm and Ardell own, has 51 acres, their son Steven farms 23 and they jointly own another 48 acres.

The family grows about 15 percent of Washington's cranberries.

"We renovate something every year," McPhail said. They replace bogs of older vines with new varieties developed at Rutgers University in New Jersey or in Wisconsin, which grows about half the U.S. crop, and, like Massachusetts, has adopted the cranberry as its state fruit.

A cranberry plant can withstand cold winters and hot summers, and will produce berries for up to a century. But newly planted vines aren't ready for harvest for three to four years

While there are some bogs with the original "MacFarland" variety in the Long Beach area, the newer hybrids can produce three or four times as many berries. The McPhails have several varieties that mature at slightly different rates, which allows them to stagger the harvest.

The new higher yielding hybrids, coupled with growth in Quebec that went from about 85 acres in 1981 to 9,500 acres now, means supply is growing faster than demand.

"We're in an oversupply situation," McPhail said.

This year the McPhails' harvest of 15,000 barrels — a barrel is 100 pounds — was down from 22,400 barrels in 2016. But cranberry yields across the state were down, possibly because of a long, wet spring, he said. Some of the

plants also had worm damage.

Some of the new varieties the McPhails have planted had good color, which can qualify for a bonus from the processor, but not high yields. Another variety, dubbed "Pilgrim," didn't color up until mid-October, and harvest didn't finish until the first week of November, about two weeks later than usual.

Farmer Malcolm McPhail operates a machine that beats the cranberries off the submerged plants in one of his bogs near Long Beach, Wash. McPhail's wife, Ardell, follows him on another beater machine.

"It was mysterious," he said of the lower yields and delayed coloring of the berries.

Prices are also down, ranging between $38 and $42 per barrel, compared to $45 or more last year.

FUN FACT NO. 4 ABOUT CRANBERRIES: *A generation ago, most of the crop was processed into juice, sauces and jelly. Now the majority of the crop is processed into dried fruit.*

"There's only so many things you can do with

cranberries," said Kim Patten, WSU extension specialist with the Pacific Northwest Cranberry Research Center in Long Beach.

As the market evolved, new varieties of cranberries were developed to meet new demands.

In the early 1900s, most cranberries were sold fresh and turned into jellies or jams by consumers, said Nicholi Vorsa, director of the Philip Marucci Blueberry and Cranberry Research and Extension Center at Rutgers University.

By the 1950s, Ocean Spray and other companies were marketing canned jellies and sauces and the crop shifted to processed food, mainly consumed at Thanksgiving when a standard feature of many holiday dinners swooshed out of a can in a perfect cylinder, was sliced and put on a plate. Because of that, the bulk of sales for cranberry products peaked in November and December.

For jellies, the amount of pectin in the berry was important and varieties were developed with higher amounts of that chemical. Pectin drops as the fruit remains on the vine, so cranberries were harvested when pectin was at its peak.

By the late 1950s, Ocean Spray, which is a cooperative of farmers, was marketing cranberry juice "cocktail," mixing the tart juice from the berries with sugar or other fruit juices such as apple or grape to provide more natural sweeteners. The amount of pectin didn't matter.

Demand increased for cranberries as a breakfast substitute for orange or apple juice, as well as a colorful mixer for bar drinks. So did supply.

Ocean Spray then began marketing dried sweetened

Farmer Malcolm McPhail drives a beater through a flooded cranberry bog. As the beater's reel strikes the submerged plants, the berries float to the surface and can be gathered by the harvest crew the next day.

cranberries the company originally developed during World War II as a food source for overseas troops. It brought them back in the 1990s through a patented process that reduced the nickel-size berries to the size of a raisin, producing Craisins while collecting the concentrated juice.

"Craisins pulled the industry out of a glut in 2000," Patten said. "Now it's saturated again."

About a fifth of all cranberries produced in the United States are still consumed the week of Thanksgiving, but the demand for traditional sauce products has dropped to the point that earlier this year Ocean Spray closed its sauce production line at Markham to concentrate on Craisins.

FUN FACT NO. 5 ABOUT CRANBERRIES: *Not all of them are cranberry red when they're ripe. Some of the berries on vines farthest from the sun are white.*

When the main demand for processed cranberries was primarily for juice blends, the color of the berries wasn't a main concern because everything was being mixed together. When the demand shifted to the fruit being dried and sweetened, color became important, Vorsa said.

New hybrids were developed that increased the yield and created a more uniform color for the ripe cranberries. That homogenous color that processors desire is only available during a certain window of the berry's development.

Harvest too soon and the color is too light; too late and it can be close to black.

But harvesting a bog isn't like picking strawberries or huckleberries, where it's possible to pick the ones that are ripe today and come back later for the ones that need a bit more time. After the bogs are flooded and the vines beaten, all the berries come off and get harvested, then the bog is drained. Containers full of berries are graded for several factors, including color, which determines the price.

The color is graded on a point system, with bonuses of up to $2.50 per barrel as it reaches the desired red. Fruit that is too dark or too light doesn't get the bonus.

New hybrids developed primarily in New Jersey and Wisconsin can double, triple or even quadruple the number of berries per plant, and produce larger, plumper fruit the drying process wants, Vorsa said. But replacing older vines with the new hybrids means a bog won't be productive for three or four years.

FUN FACT NO. 6 ABOUT CRANBERRIES: *They grow wild in many places around the world, including in Siberia, but American farmers have been the main source of commercially grown cranberries for two centuries.*

American farmers were the first to cultivate cranberries 201 years ago, and for most of that time had the market mostly to themselves. In the past 30 years, however, they've faced increasing Canadian competition, particularly from Quebec, which before 1984 had only one commercial grower and in 1992 had only 264 acres among three growers.

Last year, it had 9,500 acres of cranberries, second only to Wisconsin in total production. By comparison, Washington has about 1,600 acres, which has been fairly consistent for more than a decade.

The growth in Quebec is a result of several factors, Vorsa said. When Ocean Spray introduced the Craisin, the demand for cranberries went up and the price followed. The government of Quebec offered subsidies for its farmers to develop cranberries, and those new farms planted the new, higher-yielding varieties. Canada also allows more development than most states in wetlands, which are the natural habitat of cranberries.

Prices peaked in the 1990s, dropped in 1999, and have been up and down since then. American cranberry marketing associations are trying to increase demand in foreign countries like China, but at the same time other countries like Belarus, Azerbaijan, Chile and Argentina are starting to grow them.

FINAL FUN FACT ABOUT CRANBERRIES: *They aren't really berries at all. Technically, they're a class of fruit described as epigynous because of the way the fruit and flowers grow. They are distantly related to blueberries ... which also are an epigynous fruit.*

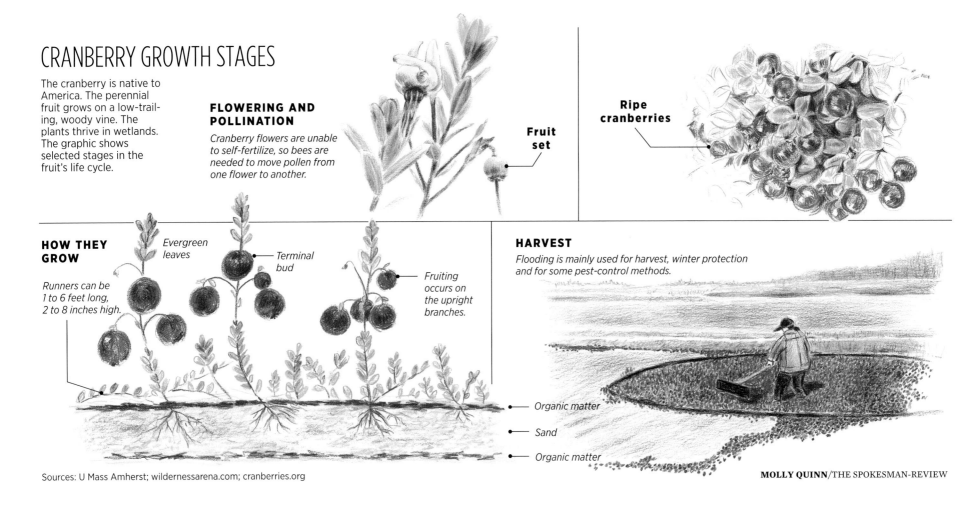

CRANBERRY GROWTH STAGES

The cranberry is native to America. The perennial fruit grows on a low-trailing, woody vine. The plants thrive in wetlands. The graphic shows selected stages in the fruit's life cycle.

FLOWERING AND POLLINATION

Cranberry flowers are unable to self-fertilize, so bees are needed to move pollen from one flower to another.

Fruit set

Ripe cranberries

HOW THEY GROW

Runners can be 1 to 6 feet long, 2 to 8 inches high.

Evergreen leaves

Terminal bud

Fruiting occurs on the upright branches.

Organic matter

Sand

Organic matter

HARVEST

Flooding is mainly used for harvest, winter protection and for some pest-control methods.

Sources: U Mass Amherst; wildernessarena.com; cranberries.org

MOLLY QUINN/THE SPOKESMAN-REVIEW

DAIRY

In the span of just a few generations, the dairy sector has moved from the milk pail and stool to industrial operations of breathtaking size. While the number of individual businesses has dropped in the Northwest and around the country, production has soared. In some places the output has more than quadrupled from the early 1980s. Innovation and technology advances continue, promising more efficiency, more automation ... and more milk.

NO DAY OFF FOR DAIRY OF FUTURE

Round-the-clock Coulee Flats operation requires efficiency, science, even nutritionist

Story by Thomas Clouse, photos by Tyler Tjomsland

THE SPOKESMAN-REVIEW

MESA, Wash. — Case VanderMeulen's oldest brother inherited his family's 100-cow dairy in the Netherlands. So the younger brother came to America and built his own milking enterprise that never sleeps.

He has 68 full-time employees who milk his 6,800 Holstein cows three times a day in two huge milking parlors. The farm also grows some of its feed and operates its own water processing plant on the sprawling 3,300-acre Coulee Flats Dairy he purchased a decade ago outside of Mesa, Wash.

Built on an existing crop farm and expanded over time, Coulee Flats operates 24 hours a day, every day, and now grosses between $30 million and $50 million a year.

"I've got milk running through my veins," VanderMeulen said. "I grew up in a dairy. It fascinated me."

VanderMeulen's fascination has led to a complex, science-based operation that takes byproducts left over from a variety of crops and mixes them with other feeds so that every cow has all the nutrition it needs to produce about 10 gallons of milk a day.

The milk from Mesa is trucked to 11 processing plants, including one in Spokane operated by Darigold, the marketing arm of the Northwest Dairy Association.

That cooperative of about 465 dairy producers in Washington, Oregon, Idaho and Montana then processes the raw milk into everything from jugs of 2 percent for the morning corn flakes to cheese, butter and powdered milk that is exported to 20 countries, including Morocco, Egypt, Japan and China.

Steve Matzen, the senior vice president of the Northwest

Dairy Association, said the farmer members of the organization has declined from about 1,600 in the 1980s to about 465 members today. It's a business that evolved from the early 1900s, when farmers still milked cows by hand.

"Our region is a great place to be a cow," Matzen said. "The climate is nice. It's a great place to grow high-quality feed."

While the number of cooperative members has dropped, production has more than quadrupled through advances in automated milkers and advances in nutrition. It's the story of conventional agriculture as large and successful farms, orchards, dairies and ranchers get bigger to supply a consistent demand for food from a growing global population.

"In the early 1980s, we produced about 2 billion pounds of milk" from the 1,600 producers, Matzen said. "Now we are producing 8.5 billion pounds."

The dairies in the regional cooperative produce about 2.3 million gallons of milk a day. All that milk is trucked by a third-party contractor to the Darigold plants, which produce about 35,000 pounds of butter every hour and 195 million pounds of cheese a year.

About 25 percent of the milk stays in liquid form and the rest gets processed into cheese, butter, yogurt and powdered milk. Of those finished products, some 40 percent are exported to other countries and 60 percent are sold to consumers in the U.S., Matzen said.

> "I've got milk running through my veins."
>
> — *Case VanderMeulen*

As a result, fluctuations in the markets anywhere in the world likely will affect the price that VanderMeulen gets paid per pound for his milk in Mesa.

"This gets back to the complexity of milk pricing," Matzen said. "The things that impact milk prices are not so much what happens in Seattle or Spokane. It's what happens around the world."

For example, prices fluctuated in 2017 after farmers, including VanderMeulen's older brother, in the 28 countries that make up the European Union started producing more milk.

"Then we saw a global imbalance," Matzen said. "So, we had downward pressure on prices."

During those times, consumers pay less for milk and producers, like Case VanderMeulen, get less money per pound, even though the cost of feed, fuel and employees may continue to rise.

"It's something that people really don't understand," Matzen said. "It's pretty impressive how hard (producers) work and what they get done. In our society today, there is such a disconnect between food production and what it takes to produce food. The appreciation just isn't there like it was 50 years ago."

Those international influences are why farmers get nervous when officials from China and the United States begin threatening a trade war, he said.

"It could have a negative impact on our farmers," Matzen said. "If all of the sudden we didn't have access to international markets, you could imagine the supply-demand imbalance."

That gets back to the reason why all the producers joined to form the cooperative, which has a staff of 1,600 people who produce, market and promote the dairy products.

"Every one of those 465 farmers are owners of the co-op," Matzen said. "Our core purpose is to provide a secure market for our member-owners. We'll be there to pick up the milk and maximize the value."

Case of milk

VanderMeulen, 52, came to the United States in 1989 and worked in California after it was clear he wasn't going to get the family dairy in Holland.

In 1991, he moved to Washington and started with a small dairy in Grandview.

He later operated two dairies in Sunnyside before looking for a new home that didn't have a growing population, as close-set dairies can cause conflict between new neighbors, and cows in confined spaces can generate a powerful odor.

VanderMeulen began looking to relocate to a place that offered a good labor market, quality roads for transporting his product and access to lots of feed. He found the land that would become Coulee Flats in 2007.

As a result, he was able to design the dairy to maximize efficiency in production and to meet strict regulations that prohibit waste from leaving the site. The dairy is just off U.S. Highway 395, west of the small town of Mesa, and the prevailing wind pushes the smell away from homeowners. It is one of about 480 dairy farms in Washington that collectively milk more than 200,000 cows.

The farm has long rows of steel roofs that provide shade for the cows in the summer and cover from the rain and snow in winter. When the temperature rises above a certain level, computers turn on sprinklers that allow the cows to cool off.

Crews are constantly moving equipment into the pens to break up the soil to make it soft for the cows, which have milking careers that average about five-and-a-half years. After that, he said, they are sold for beef.

"We treat every cow like it's our only cow," he said. "These ladies work very hard. We keep them comfortable. If they are not comfortable, they are not going to work for us very hard."

When it's time to eat, the cows walk over to long stretches of concrete slabs that are bordered by the feed bunkers. As the cattle stand and eat their ration, the farm flushes water down the concrete slabs at regular intervals. The water pushes waste downhill into huge steel grates.

That waste water is then pumped to a treatment facility, which separates out solids and sends the rest of the waste water to settling ponds where it eventually is recycled back into the system.

"We contain every ounce of water on our facility," he said.

Front-end loaders load the solid waste into trucks and it's hauled to another area of the farm, where crews drop it in long rows to compost. A huge machine that looks like a cross between a tank and a combine crawls down the rows and turns the composting waste to ensure it gets enough oxygen.

Within about three months, the compost rows are bagged and sold to landscaping crews or used on the farm as fertilizer.

Leftovers to food

To keep all those cows producing milk, crews must process and haul 370 tons of feed per day, or about 100 pounds of food every day for every cow.

"A big part of a cow's daily ration is byproducts" that are shipped by train to the Tri-Cities and trucked to Mesa, VanderMeulen said.

The feed includes what's left over from corn after it has been processed for ethanol; mill run, or leftovers from wheat after flour production; and similar byproducts from soybean, canola and cotton seeds.

One bin even had what VanderMeulen said were refried beans that had been rejected by Taco Bell.

All are mixed at varying degrees with silage — chopped,

ABOVE: Coulee Flats Dairy uses a special electronic tracker to monitor every cow on their grounds.

OPPOSITE: The sun shines on a newborn calf, one of 30 each day at Coulee Flats Dairy.

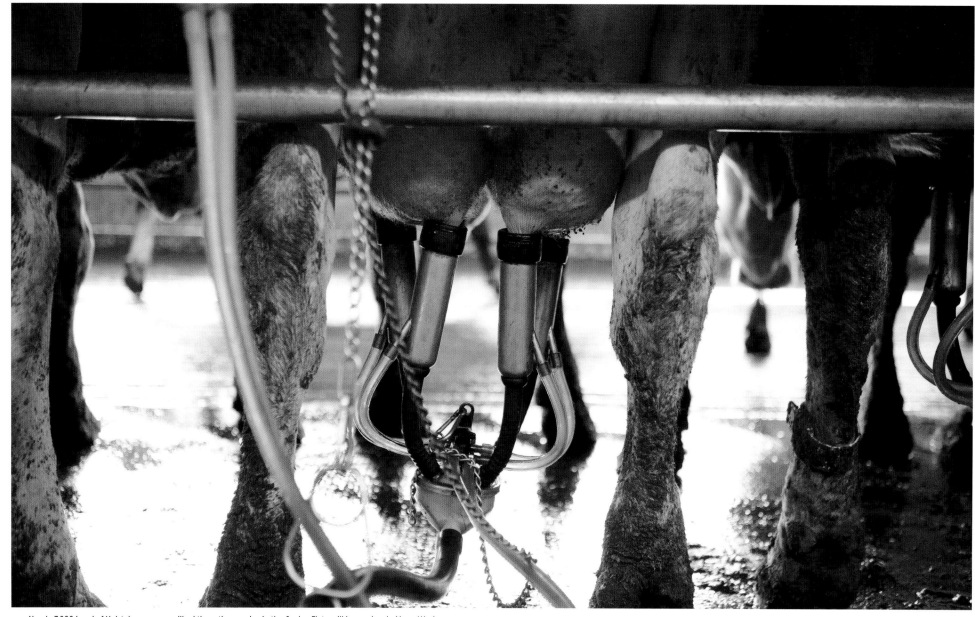

Nearly 7,000 head of Holstein cows are milked three times a day in the Coulee Flats milking parlors in Mesa, Wash.

fermented corn or other row crops that are stored under plastic. Crews also add vitamins, minerals, supplements and water to aid digestion as the food is mixed.

"Those (cows) out there are transforming byproducts, things we as humans can't digest, and making a top quality product for us," VanderMeulen said.

The portions are all dumped into huge mixing machines that create the "total mixed ration." The mixers push the feed onto a conveyer belt that transports the mixture into a waiting truck.

But it gets even more complicated. A nutritionist visits the farm every week and suggests changes in the diets of some cows. VanderMeulen installed electronic tags in every cow, and he has records that can show what that cow ate yesterday or even a month ago.

"Different groups of cows get specialized feed for where they are at in the cycle," he said.

Cows produce milk for their calves, so the farm keeps them in a perpetual cycle of pregnancy. The cows are segregated based on where they fall in that lactation cycle.

Some pens hold heifers, or young cows that have not yet had a calf, and other pens hold cows that are ready to give birth. Some cows have orange dye on their back, indicating they are not yet pregnant. Others have green, which tells

Cattle feed between milking sessions at Coulee Flats Dairy. The dairy processes about 100 pounds of food every day for every cow.

the breeder they've already been inseminated.

The farm has one employee whose sole job is to manage 30 cows that give birth every day. All those calves join about 1,500 others in separate pens. An employee feeds them from flatbed trailers containing hundreds of milk bottles.

VanderMeuelen's operation uses specialized, or "sexed" semen to artificially inseminate all the cows, ensuring that about 95 percent of the calves are girls. Any boy calves

eventually get sold for beef.

VanderMeuelen used 4001 as the number on the ear tag for the first heifer calf born on his farm. The latest ear tag, this past week, numbered 42,799.

"That's how many heifers I've produced," he said.

VanderMeuelen said it's daunting to think of the advances in the industry since he learned to milk his first cow at his family farm. He said technology is already emerging for

devices that can tell dairy owners when a cow is not feeling well or when it needs to be bred, he said.

"In 20 years from now, there will probably be a lot of cows milked by robots," he said. "It's already been done, but the technology is very expensive."

GRAPES

Already the second-largest producer in the nation, Washington state's trade in wine and wine grapes is booming: the industry has grown 8 percent a year, according to recent data. Thanks to a nearly-ideal nexus of temperature, precipitation and soil quality, that growth faces few impediments. In the meantime, the state has gained a reputation for its vintages: High quality, wide variety and all at an affordable price.

GRAPES OF RENOWN

Washington's wines are outscoring competition from around the world in quality, cost

Story by Adriana Janovich, photos by Dan Pelle

THE SPOKESMAN-REVIEW

ELTOPIA — Beneath sunlit leaves on a late morning in early autumn, grapes — plump, deep blue, veiled in a feather-light layer of fine dust — hang heavy.

Harvest has already begun. But another week — even another day or two — on these 20-year-old vines could make all the difference.

"The trick is not to get too over-anxious," said Greg Lipsker, standing between the rows of cabernet franc vines. The co-owner of Barrister Winery in Spokane has traveled to this vineyard growing atop a bluff overlooking the Columbia River northwest of Pasco, to help determine when to cut grapes from these gnarled vines.

Barrister is known for making consistently exceptional wines, particularly reds. And that's the hallmark of Washington state's wine industry: It's heralded for habitually producing high-quality wines.

Wines from this state are not only consistently outstanding, they are also more affordable than comparable wines from other top wine regions, including California, Oregon, Italy and France. Data published by Wine Spectator over the past eight years — and analyzed by the Washington Wine Commission — shows Washington state has the highest average percentage of wines rated 90 points or above compared with those other four leading wine regions, and offers them at the lowest average cost per bottle.

That's a statistic touted by Craig Leuthold, who owns Maryhill Winery with his wife, Vicki. "The best part of it is they're less expensive," he said. "Not only are they higher in quality, but they're affordable."

The Washington State Wine Commission found 46 percent of Washington wines rated by Wine Spectator from 2009 to 2016 scored 90 points or higher, compared with 45 percent for Oregon, 42 percent for France, 34 percent for Italy and 32 percent for California.

For the same time frame, those highly rated wines cost an average of $96 per bottle from France, $74 per bottle from California, $69 per bottle from Italy and $50 per bottle from Oregon.

The average price per highly rated bottle in Washington: $44.

What makes Washington wines so superb?

"In a nutshell, it's quality and diversity and value," said Craig Leuthold, who — along with Lipsker — serves on the board of the Washington Wine Institute, which advocates for Washington wineries.

"You can make bad wine out of good grapes," Leuthold said. "But there's no way you're going to make great wine out of a bad grape."

Second in the country, and still growing

Washington ranks No. 2 in the country for wine production and number of wineries. Only California makes and has more. It's home to more than 4,200 wineries, and it accounts for about 85 percent of all wine made in America.

> "In a nutshell, it's quality and diversity and value. ... There's no way you're going to make great wine out of a bad grape."
>
> — *Craig Leuthold*

Still, "I would argue we are competing with them," said Steve Warner, president of the Washington State Wine Commission. "We are certainly out-growing them."

The Washington wine industry is growing at a rate of about 8 percent per year, compared with 2 or 3 percent outside of this state, Warner said. "Over the last five years, we grew about 40 percent," he said. "You see that across the numbers — in the number of wineries, in acreage, in tonnage."

And much of its growth has occurred in the past 15 years, the past five in particular.

Last year's harvest was a record haul, with 270,000 tons of wine grapes — up more than 80,000 tons from five years ago. Ten years before that, in 2002, harvest was 115,000 tons. In 1985, it was 17,000 tons. By comparison, California vineyards last year yielded 4 million tons.

Most of the wine grapes in this state — approximately two out of every three — are used by the powerhouse Ste. Michelle Wine Estates, which dominates Washington's winescape, accounting — Warner said — for about 65 percent of the market.

In all, this state produces approximately 17.5 million cases at more than 900 wineries, up from 800 in 2013 and 700 in 2010. Most — some 87 percent — are like Barrister, producing fewer than 10,000 cases per year. But more than half — some 64 percent — are even smaller, making fewer than 1,000 cases.

In 2001, when Barrister started making wine, there were 170 wineries in Washington. Twenty years before that, in 1981, there were 19.

"We're doing really darn good," Warner said. "It's really exciting because we're a relatively youthful wine region."

Tracing grapes back to their roots

Commercial-scale plantings didn't begin until the 1960s. But Washington's wine industry traces its roots to 1825, when members of the Hudson's Bay Co. planted vines at Fort Vancouver. As immigrants from Italy, France and Germany settled the territory, they added their own plantings.

Wine grape acreage — as well as a few dozen wineries — expanded throughout the early and middle part of the 20th century. In 1937, Dr. Walter Clore, known as "the father of Washington wine," was appointed assistant horticulturist at Washington State University's Prosser extension, initiating enology and viticulture research and launching trials of hybrid grape varieties.

Commercial scale picked up in the '70s, '80s and '90s, and has been skyrocketing since. About 40 percent of the state's wine grapes have been planted in the last decade — from 31,000 acres in 2007 to about 50,000 acres today. In 1997, only some 17,000 acres were planted, up from 11,100 in 1993, or 10 years after the first American Viticultural Area, its officially designated appellation, was established.

"We saw what was happening, and we wanted to be part of it," Craig Leuthold said.

The Leutholds founded Maryhill in 1999, debuting their first vintage and opening their Goldendale tasting room in 2001. Since then, he said, the winery has seen nearly sixfold growth, "which is really incredible if you think about it." The initial goal, he said, was to produce up to 20,000 cases. "We passed that in our fourth year."

Today, Maryhill offers 60 varieties and produces some

Rows of grapes grow in the Bacchus Vineyard along the Columbia River across from the Hanford Nuclear Reservation.

80,000 cases annually. It also has two locations. Maryhill officially opened a second tasting room in November 2017. Located in Kendall Yards, it stretches nearly 5,000 square feet and offers views of the Spokane River and downtown skyline.

Across the river, Barrister has enjoyed similar advances. "The growth has been phenomenal," said Lipsker, who owns Barrister with business partners Michael White and Tyler Walters.

White and Lipsker started the winery in a 1,500-square-foot daylight basement and made just 134 cases of cabernet franc their first vintage, released in 2003, before moving the winery into a larger location. This year, Lipsker expects to produce 5,500 cases, or some 66,000

bottles, at Barrister's 26,000-square-foot event center and winery, located in a former automotive warehouse on the west end of downtown Spokane.

"We still consider ourselves a newer winery," he said. "But we're older than 80 percent of the wineries in the state."

Finding the balance

Lipsker has already brought in 110 tons of grapes this year.

It's all been about timing.

"This is such a crucial decision," said Lipsker, who contracts with 10 vineyards.

It's so crucial, in fact, that he put 1,500 miles on his car in September and another 2,000 by the end of October, making twice- and thrice-weekly trips from Spokane to Walla Walla and the Tri-Cities and beyond to check on the progress of his grapes.

Wines produced from the grapes he harvests this year won't be released for at least two years. "Could be up to four years," he said.

Lipsker pulls a gadget from his jeans pocket and places a single grape on top of the prism, then closes the plate. The refractometer reads 23, which Lipsker said "is a little higher than last time" — but not quite high enough. Lipsker knows — to the tenth of a percent — just where he wants that number to be. It's somewhere, he said, between 25 and 26 brix. The higher the brix, or sugar content, the higher the alcohol content in the wine.

"We're trying for wine that's fully developed and well-balanced and that doesn't have too much alcohol," Lipsker said, noting these grapes should be ready in another nine to 10 days. "The challenge now is to be patient."

He has several blocks of wine grapes to check. As he ambles through Bacchus Vineyard to his next stop, a row of old-growth cabernet sauvignon, he pauses to point out a cluster of smooth granite rocks. He reckons they're a result of the catastrophic floods that swept through this region at the end of the last ice age.

Ripe growth conditions

The Missoula Floods occurred repeatedly some 10,000 to 20,000 years ago, unleashing torrents of racing water that carved the scablands and many coulees of Eastern Washington. The floods left deep deposits of gravel, sand and silt throughout the Columbia Basin, creating rich agricultural land — and quite possibly the perfect terroir.

The French term refers to the set of environmental characteristics that affect a particular crop — from soil and sunlight to water, climate and farming practices. And when it comes to wines from Washington, Craig Leuthold said, "I think the quality is all about the climate. It's the soil and the climate."

The Columbia Basin is home to 99 percent of the state's vinifera acreage. These vineyards are made of well-drained, relatively low-nutrient ice-age deposits. And this type of soil allows grape vines to struggle, spread out and grow deep roots. Those deep, ramified root structures — along with well-drained soil — help account for this state's consistently good wine grapes.

Grapevines, Craig Leuthold said, "don't like to get their feet wet."

Most vineyards in the Columbia Basin lie below the high-water mark of those ancient floods and feature excellent drainage. Wind-blown sand and silt, or loess, covers layers of gravel and slack-water sediments as well

as basalt bedrock. That basalt and those granite deposits lend a particular mix of minerals to the soil.

But, as Craig Leuthold noted, soil is only one factor in terroir. The Columbia Basin lies between the 46th and 47th parallels, or approximately the same latitude as the famed Old World wine region of Burgundy. This northern location allows its vineyards up to 16 hours of daylight during growing season, or two more hours than wine grape growing regions receive in California.

The Columbia Basin also lies in the rain shadow of the Cascade Range and sees sun 300 days a year. The growing season is dry and warm, with an average daily temperature of 78 degrees. It receives little annual rainfall — about 8 inches — but experiences consistent freezing temperatures in winter, which helps combat fungus and pests.

"I can't think of anywhere in the world that's more perfect than here in Eastern Washington for growing grapes," Vicki Leuthold said. "You can just about grow anything in the right place in Washington."

Technology in the mix

Since the first Washington AVA was formed in 1983, technology has improved, and research has expanded. And growers continue to experiment with different varieties.

WINE GRAPE GROWTH STAGES

The graphic shows selected stages in the fruit's life cycle

Bud break
Buds break through on the vines. This is a vulnerable time for the plants.

Flower
About a month or two later, tiny white flowers develop.

Fruit set
After pollination a green sphere appears at the center of each flower and the flowers drop their petals.

The maximum yield is set at this stage.

Sources: visitnapavalley.com; winecoolerdirect.com

Veraison
The grape color changes from green to purple with many variations in hue during the process.

Mature wine grapes
After sugar levels and phenolic compounds are tested, the grapes are harvested.

MOLLY QUINN/THE SPOKESMAN-REVIEW

"When we first started growing grapes in Washington, farmers used the shotgun approach," said Craig Leuthold, who contracts with more than 20 growers in eight of Washington's 14 appellations, or growing regions. "Now, we're using the scientific approach to grape growing. Farmers are more sophisticated in their growing methods."

And consumers, he said, are becoming more adventurous. "It's very exciting. People are no longer afraid to try different varietals."

Grenache, Craig Leuthold said, is up and coming. So are Spanish and Italian varietals, such as albarino, tempranillo, sangiovese, dolcetta and barbera.

"We've gone from predominantly growing Riesling and chardonnay and sauvignon blanc to predominantly growing reds," Warner said. "We've seen a dramatic shift."

Bordeaux-style red blends have become more popular. "We have also seen a lot of interest in our syrah. Cabernet sauvignon, merlot and syrah, those three are growing the most year to year," Warner said.

Nearly 70 varietals are produced in Washington today. Most — some 58 percent — are reds. One of them is Barrister's petit verdot, the 2017 Red Wine of the Year, named at the nation's largest independent and scientifically organized wine competition, the Indy International. The grapes came from the sister vineyard to Bacchus, or Dionysus, first planted in 1973.

In Wine Spectator's recently released Top 100 list, a syrah from Walla Walla was named the No. 2 wine in the world for 2017. Syrah Walla Walla Valley Powerline Estate 2014 comes from winemaker Charles Smith and retails

for $45. It's one of four Washington wines to make the list, along with Smith's Sixto Chardonnay 2014 at No. 13, the Frederick Walla Walla Valley 2014 red blend at No. 39, and Gorman Zachary's Ladder Red Mountain 2014 at No. 68.

"We produce premium wine," Warner said. "We don't produce subpremium wine."

Despite its accolades, repeatedly high ratings and growth, Washington's wine industry — worth $2.067 billion to the state's economy, according to the Washington State Wine Commission — still only accounts for about 1 percent of the worldwide wine industry. Warner expects that to change shortly. "Absolutely it will," he said.

Outside the United States, Warner said, wines from Washington are seeing success in the Canadian market as well as in South Korea, China, Japan, the United Kingdom and Scandinavia. But there's still plenty of room for growth for Washington in the world of wine — globally, nationally, regionally and locally, he said

In fact, in this state, Washington wines make up only about half of the market share, a fact Warner finds particularly "annoying."

He encourages Washington wine enthusiasts to support local wineries.

"There's no reason not to," Warner said. "We're making world-class wine at a fraction of the cost. I don't see any reason why we shouldn't have 90 to 95 percent of the market.

"You should be buying Washington wine," he said. "And you should be proud of it."

RIGHT: Bins of petit verdot grapes are readying for shipping at Sagemoor Vineyard.

OPPOSITE: A worker trims away unusable bunches of petit verdot grapes in the Dionysus Vineyard north of the Tri-Cities.

Washington wine searches for an identity

Story by Adriana Janovich, photos by Dan Pelle

THE SPOKESMAN-REVIEW

Oregon has pinot noir.

Sure, it grows some 80 other varietals. But there's that one for which it is most known.

Washington grows about the same number of different kinds of wine grapes. But, said Craig Leuthold, who owns Maryhill Winery with his wife, Vicki, and serves on the board of the Washington Wine Institute, which advocates for Washington wineries, "its strength is its weakness."

"We can grow so many varietals well that we haven't been able to hang our hat on one like Oregon has done with pinot," he said, also noting "That diversity will help us in the long run."

Meantime, "We have a long way to go in terms of raising awareness of Washington wine."

Wine is produced in all 50 states, and the U.S. is the fourth-largest wine-producing country in the world, behind France, Italy and Spain. California dominates domestic wine production. But Washington's wine industry is growing faster. Still, getting the word out about its high quality and comparatively low cost is one of its biggest challenges, according to industry experts.

"The challenge is educating consumers outside of the state of Washington as to the quality of grapes in this state," said Greg Lipsker, co-owner of Barrister Winery in Spokane and another board member of the Washington Wine Institute.

Lipsker, Leuthold and Steve Warner, president of the Washington State Wine Commission, all point to the industry's relative newness as an underlying factor for marketing — as well as other — challenges.

"We're still learning," Warner said. "There's a lot that can be tweaked and dialed in."

Marketing to consumers outside this area is just one of the industry's concerns. "We're investing in viticulture and enological research to take us to the next level," Warner said.

Old World grape-growing and wine-producing regions such as France, Spain and Italy have had hundreds, even thousands, of years of experience. "They've had hundreds of thousands of tries," Warner said.

> "We can grow so many varietals well that we haven't been able to hang our hat on one like Oregon has done with pinot."
>
> — *Craig Leuthold*

Here in Washington state, most growers and winemakers have anywhere from a few decades to as few as five or 10 years. They're still fine-tuning practices and discovering what grapes grow best in particular microclimates.

"We knew we could grow wine grapes, but we didn't know which grapes were right for the different regions, latitude and slope," Warner said. "Now, we're about to zero in. Our learning has been and will continue to be more accelerated than what other regions had to go through for years and years and decades and centuries."

One of the areas of study is the effect of smoke from wildfires on wine grapes. With warm temperatures and dry conditions, Warner said, "we just think there's always going to be a concern in the future. This isn't going to go away," he said. "We need to have a plan."

Researchers at Washington State University are working to identify those effects as well as examine how to minimize them. They're experimenting with levels of intensity and different durations as well as some from native species of pine and other plants.

"You get one chance every year," Warner said. "It's not like beer or spirits."

However, in the vineyards, Warner said, the effects of smoke from wildfires don't pose the biggest challenge to Washington's wine industry. "Labor," he said, "is our biggest challenge."

Specifically, Warner said, "It's competing with other crops." Warner cited competition from hops and tree fruit as factors in pulling workers away from working in wine grapes.

Nationally, he pointed toward debate on guest-worker programs and immigration. Based on a national study, Mike Gempler, executive director of the Washington Growers League, estimates about half of all Washington farmworkers are undocumented. Comprehensive immigration reform could help stabilize, maybe even widen, the workforce.

In addition to competition for — and a shortage of — labor, the cost is also going up. At the very least, farmworkers make minimum wage, which in Washington is $11, one of the highest in the country. Washington's minimum wage is slated to increase annually during the next three years: $11.50 in 2018, $12 in 2019, and $13.50 in 2020.

And the market is getting more competitive.

"California wineries are coming up," Leuthold said. "Canada is coming down."

Acreage here is available at a fraction of the cost of land in California. And, in older wine grape growing regions — such as California's Napa Valley — there isn't much, if any, room to grow, Warner said. "There's no new acreage in Napa. Napa's planted out," he said. "We have new acreage available. We have acreage that can be converted from other crops. We have room to grow."

Despite all the recent growth in Washington wine, three major companies dominate the industry. Accounting for approximately 80 percent of the state's wine landscape are: Constellation, whose brands include Hogue Cellars

At an historic warehouse in downtown Spokane, volunteers crush syrah grapes for Barrister Winery as a train rolls past Railroad Avenue.

and Charles Smith, among others; Precept, whose brands include Canoe Ridge, Waterbrook and Sagelands, among others; and Ste. Michelle, which formed in 1967 and celebrated its 50th anniversary last year. Chateau Ste. Michelle, its flagship and the state's largest winery, produces some 3.4 million cases annually.

The majority of Washington's wineries — some 64 percent — sell fewer than 1,000 cases per year.

Warner predicts growth in Washington's wine industry will continue.

"If you look at past data, we continued to grow through the recession. We saw no downturn in the number of tons harvested, the number of acres planted or the number of wineries coming on board," he said. "People like to drink wine to celebrate and to mourn, if they're happy or sad. Generally, people tend to kind of like wine."

And, despite some challenges in Washington's up-and-coming wine industry, "There's just so much opportunity out there," Warner said. "All signs are pointed in the right direction. All signs are pointed up."

HOPS

Hops farmers face the same challenges as growers of everything from apples to onions: labor shortages, rising costs, and a particularly pesky mite. These are high barriers that keep new players from entering the market. But craft beer has propelled the industry to greater recognition around the world and an explosion of hop acreage in the Yakima Valley.

BUMPER HOPS

Washington is the top source of this key craft beer ingredient

Story by Rachel Alexander, photos by Kathy Pionka

THE SPOKESMAN-REVIEW

YAKIMA — Whether your brew of choice is Budweiser or Bale Breaker, there are few places on Earth where you can sip a cold pint knowing the flavors came from a farm just down the road.

That's a point of pride for nearly everyone connected to the Yakima Valley's hops industry, from farmers to regulars at Yakima Sports Center — a downtown bar with a selection of two dozen craft beer taps.

Hops farmers are still farmers, and face the same challenges as other growers: labor shortages, rising costs, a particularly pesky mite, high barriers to entry that keep new players from entering the market.

But the rise of craft beer has propelled the industry, and Yakima along with it, to greater recognition around the world. Washington hop acreage has grown 42 percent over the past five years, with 38,438 acres harvested in 2017, according to Hop Growers of America.

That increase has paralleled an explosion in the craft beer industry and the dominance of India pale ales, the style best known for showcasing hop flavors.

It's a Northwest, and especially a Washington crop: The Evergreen State made up 74 percent of U.S. hop production in 2017. Add Oregon and Idaho, and the Pacific Northwest accounted for 98 percent.

Worldwide, 41 percent of the hops produced in 2017 were American. The only other country that comes close is Germany, at 36 percent.

Why Yakima? Like many crops, hops are fussy about where they grow best.

Long daylight hours in the summer are important for

the plant to bloom, producing the green cones that go into beer. That requirement has concentrated the plant almost entirely within a narrow latitude band in the Northern Hemisphere, from Washington to Germany and the Czech Republic.

But they also need a dry climate: Too much moisture and the plant will mold, ruining the flavor of the hops. That rules out much of the Pacific Northwest.

"We have a very unique kind of climate and region," said Patrick Smith, a fourth-generation hop farmer who runs Loftus Ranches with his father, Mike. Some people in the industry say Yakima has the right terroir, a term borrowed from wine grape growers to describe the impact of a region's climate and soil on the grape flavor.

The youngest generation of the Smith family shows the effect hops have had on Yakima over the past decade.

Patrick Smith is the oldest of three siblings, and said all three were eager to get out of central Washington after high school.

"It was like, 'Bye, I'm going to the big city, see you at Thanksgiving, Yakima,'" Smith said.

His sister, Meghann, and brother, Kevin, followed him out to the University of Washington. But as the cost of living rose in larger cities and craft beer, especially India pale ales, became cool, the siblings started realizing they had grown up somewhere special.

Meghann Quinn, the middle sibling, is now the business manager at Bale Breaker Brewing Co., the only U.S. commercial brewery located on a commercial hops farm. More specifically, they're on Field 41 of Loftus Ranches, hence the name of their flagship Field 41 Pale Ale.

"

"This was a yellow beer town."

—Meghann Quinn

They opened in 2013 with a vision of supplying quality craft beer to Eastern Washington, Quinn said. At the time, Yakima had only one small craft brewery and people thought they'd have no luck selling their product outside of Seattle.

"People just thought we were crazy," she said. "This was a yellow beer town."

Every Bale Breaker flagship brew is hoppy: several IPAs and a pale ale that would pass as an IPA at most breweries. (There's no fine line distinguishing the two, though a pale ale tends to be slightly less alcoholic and hoppy.)

"We wanted to teach people that hoppy doesn't have to mean bitter," Quinn said. Topcutter, their main IPA, is milder than you might expect, with lots of hops giving it a bit of sweet citrus flavor.

Smith, 34, took over the 1,800-acre farm. It's one of about 40 operations in Washington that collectively grow three-quarters of American hops and provide the backbone for the state's $1.8 billion craft beer industry.

Harvest on the crop won't begin until late August. But spring is the most labor-intensive time of year for growers.

Workers first tie the ropes to the overhead trellis, moving down the rows quickly while tying cow hitches with one hand. Then the hop vines are "trained" — individually curved up a rope so they can grow skyward, moving clockwise as they follow the sun.

"It's truly a very skilled labor by farmworkers," said Doug Walsh, a hops researcher and entomologist at Washington State University's Irrigated Agriculture Research and Extension Center.

Ideally, the vines will reach the top of the trellis between the summer solstice and the Fourth of July. That ensures they're ready to harvest around September.

"Getting this right, the timing, might be the single most important thing we do," Smith said.

The result can be breathtaking. The overgrown vines of Field 15 look like a jungle near dusk, with the ryegrass cover crop sticking to shoes between planted rows.

Tendrils of hops rise 8 or 9 feet in the air, snaking up twisted coconut fiber ropes toward the trellis 18 feet above the earth.

It's dry, hot like summer though it's only May. The hops are drip-irrigated and the sun has been beating down all day, but the earth gives off the sandy-sweet aroma of freshly rained-on soil.

Wooden poles give a semblance of plan, lining the rows and separating plants into clusters of eight. Vines like to grow thick, running together, adding curve to the grid.

This field of Simcoe hops has grown too quickly and will likely need to be re-trained. But as the sun sets, it's the perfect place to appreciate the beauty of one of Yakima's most charismatic crops.

To understand the impact craft beer has had on hops, you have to understand how beer is made.

There are thousands of variations and small details that distinguish styles from each other, but the basic process remains the same. Take grain, usually barley, and steep in hot water to release the sugars. Boil the resulting liquid, called wort, adding hops and other spices for flavor. Ferment with yeast, transforming the sugars into carbon dioxide, then bottle the resulting beer.

Hops traditionally have been added to beer as a bittering agent, to balance out the sweet flavors from the malt. That's the role they play in American-style lagers and American-style pilsners: the terms for brews like Coors and Miller.

The varieties that do that work best are called "bittering" hops and include Columbus, Zeus and Tomahawk, collectively known as CZT hops.

Hops used in hop-forward beers are called "aroma" hops and include Cascade, a staple in Pacific Northwest beers, and newer varieties like Citra, Mosaic and Galaxy. Some varieties, like Simcoe, are dual-purpose, meaning they both bitter and add flavor.

Since 2012, the makeup of hops fields has shifted substantially, with aroma varieties on the rise. Cascade remains the most popular hop by acreage, while Zeus has fallen from

The sun sets over field 15 as hops plants grow onto coconut fiber ropes at Loftus Ranches, a fourth-generation hop farm in the Yakima Valley.

second place, with 3,277 acres, to fifth, with 2,214. Columbus and Tomahawk have seen similar declines, moving from fourth place to 10th.

Taking their places: Citra, the third most popular hop in 2017, which is known for adding a juicy, citrus profile that's popular in IPAs right now. Simcoe, a dual-purpose hop found in many local beers, has moved from ninth place to fourth, with 3,753 acres planted in 2017. Mosaic, another aroma hop, cracked the top 10 list in 2015 and now has 1,877 acres planted.

"Citra is probably the fastest-growing hop variety that we had ever seen," said Ann George, executive director of Hop Growers of America.

Left alone, a hop plant can produce for about eight years, said Jaki Brophy, communications manager for Hop Growers of America. But it's rare to find a field in Yakima where a single variety is planted for so long. Growers are

shifting fields and planting new varieties in response to brewer demand.

"The average life of a hop field in the Yakima Valley has been cut in half," Smith said.

Craft beer is a small share of U.S. consumption — roughly 13 percent by volume in 2017, according to the Brewers Association. But on average, those brewers use far more hops per barrel than their macro counterparts, especially when making IPAs and pale ales.

The rapid growth of craft breweries made it difficult for some brewers to get the hop varieties they wanted several years ago, especially after a 2015 drought hit the Yakima crop.

George said speaking of an overall hops shortage or oversupply is usually too simplistic, since hops are grown under contract. Farmers sell their product to processors and distributors: roughly a half-dozen companies that dominate the Yakima market and sell their wares to brewers, typically as dry pellets or extracts.

Some breweries also contract directly with farmers for hops, George said. They may be larger beer producers that have the scale, or they may be craft operations that have a very specific flavor profile they want and have developed a relationship with a farmer.

Most contracts are for five years, because setting up a field for a specific variety is labor-intensive. Hops have to be propagated by cutting from the plant's rhizome, the root mass, which then grows as a start until it's transplanted to the field. Farmers then set up the wooden poles and trellis, and run irrigation lines.

It's a lot of up-front cost that farmers want to amortize over several seasons, George said.

"When a brewer walks in your door and says, 'I want this,' you have about a two-year time lag before you can give them 100 percent of this," she said.

That problem is illustrated — somewhat — in the Wi-Fi password at Perry Street Brewing, the Perry District microbrewer known for making hop-forward beers.

As they prepared to open in 2013, owner and brewer Ben Lukes wanted to buy Simcoe hops, which were just beginning their rise in popularity. Washington acreage would jump 60 percent in 2015.

Lukes found that the distributor representative he worked with was unable to get him any. He's since begun working with another rep, and concedes the issue might have been a combination of availability and the unhelpfulness of the first rep. But the story stuck, and the taproom's password is "nosimcoe."

"At the time hops were really short and that was proprietary," he said. Now, Simcoe is in many brews at Perry Street.

George said one function of the growers association is to help brewers better understand how hops are grown and the production realities for farmers. The situation is more stable now, she said, with varieties that had been difficult to get becoming readily available.

"For a few years we were playing catch-up because the brewery industry was growing at a more rapid rate,"

George said.

If craft beer were to fade away, that would also spell disaster for hop growers, but no one in Yakima seemed concerned about that possibility.

Though much has been made of people growing tired of hoppy beer, IPAs still dominate the craft sales market, and craft beer consumption grew last year even as overall U.S. beer consumption fell slightly.

"Craft is certainly not a fad. It's definitely got some staying power," said Pete Mahony, vice president of supply chain operations for John I. Haas, one of the largest hops distributors in the world. The company processed 104 million pounds of Northwest hops last year.

Smith left Yakima in 2000 after high school, convinced he would never come back. He and his two younger siblings all wanted to get off the farm and into a bigger city.

"Yakima was not a super-exciting place to be and the hops industry wasn't a super-exciting place to be," Smith said. But as craft beer got popular and places like Seattle became more expensive, Smith found himself reconsidering. He

HOP GROWTH STAGES The graphic shows selected stages in the life cycle of the hop.

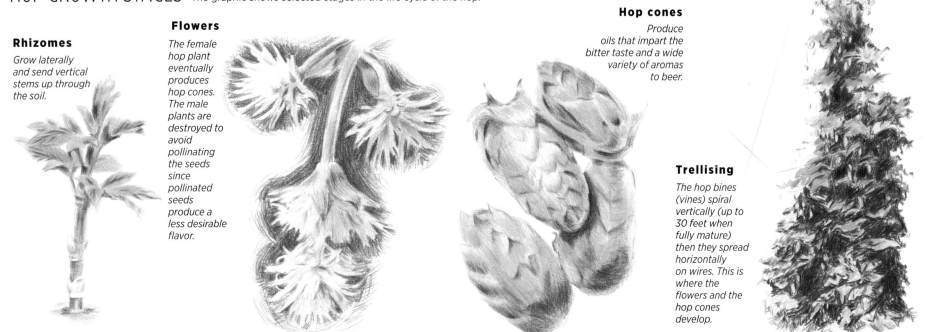

Rhizomes
Grow laterally and send vertical stems up through the soil.

Flowers
The female hop plant eventually produces hop cones. The male plants are destroyed to avoid pollinating the seeds since pollinated seeds produce a less desirable flavor.

Hop cones
Produce oils that impart the bitter taste and a wide variety of aromas to beer.

Trellising
The hop bines (vines) spiral vertically (up to 30 feet when fully mature) then they spread horizontally on wires. This is where the flowers and the hop cones develop.

Sources: gardeningknowhow.com; fifthseasongardening.com

MOLLY QUINN/THE SPOKESMAN-REVIEW

moved back to take over the farm, while his younger siblings run Bale Breaker Brewing. It is, as far as they know, the only brewery in the U.S. operating on a commercial hop farm.

Smith said he's seen Yakima change as the industry has grown. It's becoming a destination for beer tourism, having finally developed enough craft breweries to sustain interest. At hop harvest time, brewers from around the world converge on central Washington for hop selection.

"In the beer geek world, it'd be like going to the Oscars red carpet," he said.

ABOVE: Beer is tested in the labratory at Bale Breaker Brewing Company.

OPPOSITE: Kevin and Meghann Quinn talk about the business of running Bale Breaker Brewing Company.

ONIONS

From 19th-century Corsica down through generations of horticultural tinkerers, the Walla Walla sweet onion — official vegetable of the state of Washington — has cultivated deep roots in the valley and a reputation far beyond. Yet in more recent decades, advances in transportation and a growing, year-round demand has seen competition rise from every corner of the nation. In this new reality, Washington's farmers face a stark choice: Get big — or get out.

WASHINGTON'S SWEET SPOT

Walla Walla Valley's low-sulfur soils help give namesake onion its distinct flavor

Story by Rachel Alexander, photos by Jesse Tinsley

THE SPOKESMAN-REVIEW

Before Walla Walla became known for wine, it was famous for something else: "Home of the onion so sweet you can eat it like an apple."

That line, a mainstay of marketing materials for the Walla Walla sweet onion, graces the official promotional website for what is the official state vegetable.

Though true, it's a bit exaggerated: While the onion is enjoyed raw, most people put thick slices on burgers or in salads rather than munching on the whole globe.

Michael J. Locati, a fourth-generation farmer descended from the Italian immigrants who first raised the onion in Walla Walla, is an exception.

"Every field, I usually try to eat an onion," he said.

Locati, 27, has taken over the region's largest onion-producing farm from his uncle, Michael F. Locati. He studied agricultural technology and business management at Washington State University and worked off the farm a few years before returning.

Onion farmers have dealt with the same pressure facing growers across Washington: get big or get out. Locati is part of a consortium that owns its own packing shed, and farms about 350 of the region's roughly 500 acres, making the consortium by far the largest grower of Walla Walla Sweets.

Still, sweet onions remain a do-it-yourself heirloom crop in most ways. Farmers save their own seeds, and plants have been selected over generations of onions for desired traits: large globes, sweet flavor and winter hardiness.

Much of what happens in the fields is the result of tinkering by individual farmers.

OPPOSITE: Farmworkers stop for a break in an onion field in Touchet, Wash. Mostly Hispanic workers manually lift and trim thousands of pounds of the popular seasonal onions every two days.

"There's no onion like this," Locati said.

Sweet start

The onion's Italian roots are still visible in the names of the region's growers, many of whom are third- or fourth-generation descendants of the gardeners who bred the first Walla Walla Sweets. The Locatis are the biggest, but other growers include the Arbinis and Castoldis.

The official origin story for the onion is partially the result of educated guesswork undertaken by Joe J. Locati, a former district horticultural inspector and a descendant of the first Locati generation to grow the vegetable. Interviewing his uncle, he wrote down the family's story about the onion's origin in a 1976 essay, preserved in the Penrose Library archives at Whitman College.

The genesis of the Sweets can be traced to a Frenchman named Peter Pieri. He was a soldier stationed on the island of Corsica in the late 1800s with plans to move to Walla Walla. He'd heard the small town was good for gardening. He brought the onion seed prevalent in Corsica with him, and other Italian gardeners in the valley started growing it.

As Joe Locati recounts, the onion originally was planted for harvest in the fall, but not every onion sold, and farmers let them winter over.

"It was discovered, in this manner, that they were winter hardy," he wrote.

Early accounts sometimes referred to the onion as a French variety brought to Walla Walla by an Italian immigrant. Joe Locati points out the irony of that account, since his research suggests the opposite: Pieri was a Frenchman, and the onion's origin in Corsica made it Italian by heritage, if not by geopolitical boundaries.

A second strain of the onion came over with Giovanni Arbini, who migrated to Walla Walla from his native Italy around 1890. He did much of the early work refining the onion and selected varieties that matured in early June, weeks ahead of the usual July harvest.

Italian gardeners planted small fields of vegetables, with the sweet onion leading the way for the cottage industry.

"That variety, more than any other commodity, was responsible for the continuance and survival of the truck garden industry for more than 70 years," Joe Locati wrote.

Extending harvest

The original Walla Walla Sweet, planted in September, stays underground during the winter and begins to put

> "That variety, more than any other commodity, was responsible for the continuance and survival of the truck garden industry for more than 70 years."
>
> — *Joe Locati*

up stalks in the spring. They're ready for harvest when the green stalks of the plant start to fall over, Locati said, typically in early June.

The problem? That overwinter onion harvest usually lasts only a few weeks, ending sometime in July. That makes it a difficult crop for farmers to market.

"Costco's not going to buy onions if you're only two weeks," Locati said.

To extend their season, Walla Walla onion farmers use transplanted and spring-seeded onions.

Sarah McClure and her husband, Dan, grow about 28 acres of organic sweet onions and sell to natural markets and grocery stores. Every year, they ship seeds to Arizona over the winter and get back small plants that look like salad onions in March. The onions arrive back at the farm in small bundles and are replanted. The replanted onions will be available when the winter sweets stop producing.

Many farmers, including Locati, also plant spring sweets in March to harvest at the end of the season. That keeps growers in business until August.

The hope is to get the first crops out of the ground in time to hit stores by the Fourth of July.

"If we miss that July Fourth market and we don't have onions available then, it's really hard to catch up because everyone wants a big slab of sweet onions on their burgers on the Fourth of July," Sarah McClure said.

Location matters

The onion's characteristic sweetness is related to its water and sugar content, as well as the soil it's grown in. Sweets have a higher water content, making them unsuitable for long storage. They're also more sugary.

Most importantly, they have lower levels of pyruvic acid, the sulfur-containing compound that gives onions their distinctive pungency. Sweet onion varieties tend to have concentrations below 5 percent, while regular yellow onions

BATTLE OF THE SWEET ONIONS

Most American sweet onions are the result of crossbreeding and tinkering with two types of yellow onions: the Grano and the Granex. Walla Walla Sweets are the exception, since their seed stock was imported from Corsica in the early 1900s.

WALLA WALLA SWEET

Bred by Italian gardeners who immigrated to the Walla Walla Valley in the late 1800s, it was designated Washington's state vegetable in 2007.

Region: Walla Walla County and parts of Umatilla County, Oregon.

First planted: 1920s

VIDALIA

Vidalias were the first sweet onion grown in the U.S. after the Walla Walla Sweet began cultivation. They're available in the spring and summer and typically hit shelves before Walla Walla Sweets.

Region: Restricted to 13 counties and portions of seven counties in southeastern Georgia.

First planted: 1930s

MAUI

Farmers on the Hawaiian island of Maui maintain the volcanic soil gives their sweet onions a distinctive taste. They're available most of the year on the island, from mid-February to late November.

Region: Maui, Hawaii

First planted: 1943

TEXAS 1015

This onion was developed by Dr. Leonard Pike, a horticulture professor at Texas A&M University, after decades of work to optimize the sweet onion through crossbreeding. In an interview with Texas Monthly, Pike said part of the goal was to develop a better onion for making onion rings.

Region: Texas

First planted: 1980s

IMPERIAL SWEETS

Farmers in the country's top onion-producing state grow several varieties in the fertile Imperial Valley. Sweet onions are available from late April to early June. The city of Imperial holds a Sweet Onion Festival in April.

Region: Imperial Valley, California

First planted: 1930s

Sources: Texas Monthly, Vidalia Onion Committee, Maui Now, New York Times

THE SPOKESMAN-REVIEW

are typically above 10 percent.

The Walla Walla Valley's low-sulfur soils help give the onion its distinct sweet flavor. Farmers maintain that if you took the seed outside of Walla Walla and planted it in, say, a Spokane garden, the resulting onion wouldn't be a true Walla Walla Sweet.

In 1995, the U.S. Department of Agriculture issued a federal marketing order giving the Walla Walla Sweet region-protected status. An onion must be grown in defined boundaries within Walla Walla County and its southern neighbor, Umatilla County in Oregon, to be marketed as a Walla Walla Sweet.

There's no well-funded crop research center in Washington for sweet onions. Instead, most agricultural research focuses on storage varieties of onions grown in the Columbia Basin, said Tim Waters, a regional vegetable specialist with Washington State University based in Pasco.

The state's onion crop covers some 24,000 acres, making Sweets just over 2 percent of the state's harvest, at 523 acres.

"It's quite small, but in terms of marketing they've got the niche," Waters said.

Perhaps no one is more passionate about the Walla Walla Sweet than Kathy Fry-Trommald, the now-retired executive director of the Walla Walla sweet onion Marketing Committee. Before leaving the post in June, Fry-Trommald spent 16 years traveling the country to promote the signature Washington onion, which was grown on 1,400 acres in its heyday.

There was a time when Walla Walla Sweets were the only sweet onion available west of the Mississippi, she said. Before produce was a global business, Vidalia onions grown in Georgia were available on the East Coast and Walla Walla Sweets dominated the rest of the country. It wasn't economical to ship across the country.

That changed in the early 2000s, when grocery stores started demanding a year-round sweet onion, she said. Shipping produce around the world got cheaper, and Vidalias, which are available earlier in the season, started appearing in the Northwest.

It's not possible to grow a year-round sweet onion in any

Farmer Michael J. Locati cuts open a jumbo sweet onion in a field in Touchet, Wash.

one part of the U.S., so new varieties started springing up: the Maui in Hawaii, the Imperial Valley Sweet in California and the Sweetie Sweet in Nevada.

"We don't have our window anymore like we used to. Walla Walla Sweets used to have a few weeks in the summer where we didn't have a lot of competition, but now it seems like every state in the country has a sweet onion they put out," said Paul Castoldi, a third-generation Walla Walla Sweet farmer.

Fry-Trommald said those onions, many of which were developed by university crop research centers, just aren't as good as a true Walla Walla Sweet. Few things make her as angry as imposter onions, she said.

"People will take any old onion and put it in a Walla Walla bag," she said, a practice illegal under the federal marketing order. She recalled seeing a sign in a Whole Foods store recently advertising "LOCAL Pennsylvania Organic Walla Walla sweet onions," a label so nonsensical that Fry-Trommold simply shook her head.

The increased availability of other types of onions has made life harder for growers. It's one factor behind the onion's declining acreage, which has hovered around 500 acres for the past few seasons. The other reasons are common across farms all over Washington: younger generations who don't want to take over the family business and increased costs of labor.

"A lot of young people got out of it because of the money. It's too volatile now, too up-and-down to rely on the income," Castoldi said. His farm is one of the exceptions: He's working the land with his brother, Bob, and his nephew, Nathan, who's in his 30s and planning to take over.

While sweets were once the mainstay of Italian immigrants' gardens, today the crop is typically one piece of a diversified business. Like many crops, onions are rotated to preserve soil nutrients. The Castoldis, McClures and Locatis all grow other crops: alfalfa, pea and corn seed, asparagus and other vegetables.

Locati knows he's one of a few people his age taking over the onion business, but he's eager to keep the family tradition alive.

"You survive this long, you can't fail now. It'd be embarrassing."

ONION GROWTH CYCLE

Onions germinate and grow slowly.
They have a shallow root system
that mustn't be injured.
The growth cycle ranges from
120 to 180 days depending on the
variety of onion.

Germination

*Cotyledon (embryonic leaf)
appears. It looks like an arch.*

First leaf

First leaf emerges.

Cotyledon fall

*Second and third leaves appear.
Cotyledon falls.*

Fall of first leaf

*First and second leaves dry out and fall.
Other leaves appear.*

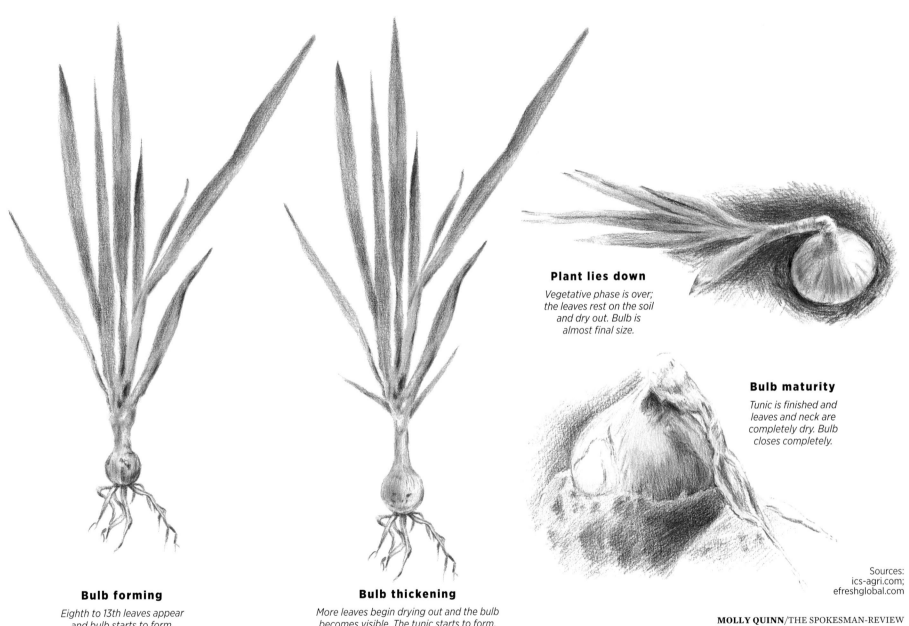

Bulb forming

Eighth to 13th leaves appear and bulb starts to form.

Bulb thickening

More leaves begin drying out and the bulb becomes visible. The tunic starts to form.

Plant lies down

Vegetative phase is over; the leaves rest on the soil and dry out. Bulb is almost final size.

Bulb maturity

Tunic is finished and leaves and neck are completely dry. Bulb closes completely.

Sources:
ics-agri.com;
efreshglobal.com

MOLLY QUINN/THE SPOKESMAN-REVIEW

Growers rely on dwindling immigrant workforce to harvest onions

Story by Rachel Alexander, photos by Jesse Tinsley
THE SPOKESMAN-REVIEW

It takes a crew of onion pickers just a few hours to transform a field from a sea of knee-high green to a dusty-brown collection of onion bulbs.

After farmers drive over with a tractor to undercut the bulbs, workers stream through, grabbing the loose onions and pulling them up. By late June, the harvest has been pushed back as early as 3 a.m. so crews can finish before the worst heat of the day begins.

The field takes on the sweet, slightly pungent smell of a fresh onion as workers make a second pass. Bent over, they grab a fistful of onions with practiced hands and shear the tops off, throwing the bulbs into a nearby box.

"Harvesting onions the way we do it is one of the hardest jobs there is," said Harry Hamada, a second-generation onion farmer who manages the Walla Walla River Packing Shed. Few crops, aside from asparagus, demand as much repetitive, bent-over labor.

But after 30 years in the fields, Mauro Lopez said it's not so bad.

"I have experience. I can't say it's very hard," he said, speaking in Spanish.

Lopez, 57, came to Walla Walla in 1986 through a contractor to harvest Walla Walla Sweets. He's a native of Oaxaca, Mexico, a state in southern Mexico bordering the Pacific Ocean where many U.S. farm workers come from.

Unlike many in the industry, Lopez is a U.S. citizen. He and his wife have a house in Walla Walla, and his daughter

just graduated from Eastern Washington University with her teaching certificate, which causes him to beam with pride.

"All my life, I've worked here in the fields so my daughter can get ahead," he said.

Lopez said the majority of onion harvesters he's worked with over the years are in the U.S. illegally, though growers require a Social Security number from employees. He doesn't think it's likely those workers will be able to apply for amnesty or legal status in the U.S.

"I don't think they're going to give papers," he said, referring to the federal government under President Donald Trump.

Hamada grew up working on his uncle's onion farm. His parents and uncle lived in Kent, Wash., before World War II, but were interned during the war as people of Japanese heritage. They lost the farm and had nothing to go back to, so they moved to the Walla Walla area to farm after the war ended.

Vertical integration through the packing shed is one reason they've been able to stay in business. He and his brothers invested in their first packing facility around 1992 to give them more control over the final product being shipped to stores.

OPPOSITE: Workers at the Walla Walla River Packing Company load fresh Walla Walla sweet onions onto a refrigerated truck at their packing plant near Walla Walla, Wash. The plant processes the majority of sweet onions in the region. When they arrive from the field, they are put in the drying shed to dry out the stems, helping preserve them for their trip to market.

RIGHT: After arriving from the field and dried, onions are sorted for size and trained eyes look for defects, such as nicks made during harvest.

If supermarkets don't like the quality of the onion, "it all falls back on the grower," Hamada said. The current shed opened around 2000 to give them more space.

During harvest, a crew of about 60 people dries, sorts, packs and loads the onions. Women work on an inspection line, finding reject onions with cuts or blemishes that will be destined for fast food. Men drive forklifts, loading the semitrucks destined for Albertsons and Costco.

Earlier this summer, a few young men loading onions into bags were working in the plant as a summer job. Diego, who did not want to give his last name, said he'll be heading to EWU in the fall to study business. He works with another young man shoving small, consumer-size bags of medium onions into boxes to ready them for shipping.

Onion farmers say labor is increasingly a challenge for them. Harvesting the globes is labor-intensive, and farmers face dual pressures: increased costs due to a rising minimum wage, and more difficulty filling open jobs.

This season, Hamada installed a new labor-saving machine that automates part of the sorting process, allowing him to cut the crew by about 10 people. He said he made the decision before the minimum wage went up, but that validated his decision.

Michael J. Locati, a fourth-generation sweet onion farmer who's recently taken over his family's share in the main growing consortium, said his workers asked for an increase in their piece rate, which is based on how much they harvest.

Workers are paid per 50-pound box they fill, and experienced workers can earn well above minimum wage, especially if the onions are larger. Because the state minimum wage was raised to $11 an hour at the beginning of the year, Locati gave his workers about a 20 percent raise on their piece rate this season.

He's not opposed to the increase, but said people in urban areas need to recognize it's going to impact the cost to produce their food.

"That's great," he said of the increase. "I think everyone deserves to be successful, but it doesn't mean you're not going to have to pay more."

Hamada and Locati are part of the same growing consortium, which raises about 350 of the roughly 500 acres of Walla Walla Sweets in the area. This year, for the

first time, they've brought in 13 workers on H-2A visas, which are for temporary agricultural workers.

Farmers often shy away from the visa program, which requires employers to house workers, transport them and guarantee a prevailing wage above the state minimum (though most will earn more at the piece rate). But Locati said this year they wanted to try it because workers have gotten harder to find.

Longtime workers like Lopez were part of a generation that was able to get amnesty and citizenship. They raised children who got an education and have choices besides working in onion fields. Locati doesn't fault anyone for wanting better; it's the same thing his grandparents did. But he said immigration restrictions have made it difficult for farmers to get a new generation of workers.

"We're not getting replacements because it's so hard to get across the border, it's so hard to get a visa," Locati said.

The onion harvest season overlaps with apples and cherries, so farmers compete for a scarce labor pool.

"Our government thinks that Americans will do that work. They're kidding themselves," Hamada said.

Labor isn't the only difficulty growers face.

Increased competition from other sweet onions has made their product more difficult to sell, and Hamada worries about the future of the crop since many growers are aging out.

"Everything's a challenge," Hamada said with a laugh.

AUTHENTIC
WALLA WALLA SWEET ONIONS

Arbini Farms
A FAMILY TRADITION
SINCE 1899

WALLA WALLA
SWEET
ONIONS

Sweet Lou keeps onion on minds of residents, visitors

Story by Rachel Alexander, photos by Tyler Tjomsland

THE SPOKESMAN-REVIEW

Throwing out the ceremonial first pitch is a standard part of any baseball game.

But Walla Walla is probably the only place in the world that throws a sweet onion.

Borleske Stadium, home of the West Coast League's Walla Walla Sweets, is just one of a handful of places around town where visitors are reminded of the region's connection to Washington's state vegetable.

Though the town has gained prominence as a wine tourism destination, with world-class restaurants and tasting rooms taking up much of the downtown real estate, the city has a few onion-related quirks.

One is a tradition at Whitman College, dating back to the early 1990s, where the admissions office mails a box of sweet onions over the summer to each student in the incoming freshman class.

John Bogley, the college's vice president of development and alumni relations, said the tradition was inspired by an alumnus of the college, Carl Schmitt, who ran a bank in Palo Alto, California. Every year, he had a truckload of onions delivered to the bank as a thank-you to customers for their business. Schmitt told the story to then-college president Tom Cronin, who adopted it.

The onions are packed in the field in boxes of six, then mailed to students with a letter explaining their origin. Locati Farms supplies the onions now, though Whitman has used different suppliers in the past, Dean of Admissions Tony Cabasco said.

"We really want to find ways to celebrate Walla Walla and the community here, and I think that's kind of a nice way to also do that," he said.

ABOVE: Parks Basel, 2, wears his Sweets hat to the ballpark. The West Coast League team is named for Walla Walla's signature farm product, the sweet onion.

OPPOSITE: On the side streets of Walla Walla, Wash., signs and stands pop up as soon as the sweet onions start coming in from the fields.

Every year, he said, he gets a few calls from students in the spring who have been admitted and want to know where their onions are. Cabasco has to explain that they're only for students who actually decide to enroll.

International students can't receive them thanks to the difficulty of shipping produce abroad. Cabasco said some students receive their box, which has holes in it, and think the college has sent them a hamster or small dog.

The annual cost to the college is about $10,000 a year, and shipping costs more than the onions themselves. The tradition was on a list of nonessential programs considered for cuts during the 2008 recession, when the college's financial aid needs rose, but Cabasco said the entire office was opposed.

"It's a thing at Whitman, and we can't not do it," he said.

For the Walla Walla Sweets, onions aren't just a projectile. They're the core of the baseball team's brand.

The team's mascot is Sweet Lou, a surprisingly endearing winking onion with legs who roams around the stadium high-fiving kids and runs a number of contests between innings. He frequently races children around the bases, though thanks to his size 19 feet, he rarely wins those contests.

The Sweets' website describes him as the "friendliest and most energetic onion you'll ever meet," noting that he sleeps in an onion patch at night but otherwise lives at the ballpark.

Sweets President Zachary Fraser declined an interview request on behalf of Sweet Lou.

"Lou's a silent onion," Fraser explained. "He needs an interpreter."

Fraser moved to Walla Walla to form the team in 2009, and worked with a sports branding agency to come up with the Sweets brand. He had the finished logo done before fans officially voted on a team name, but fortunately the signature onion won by a wide margin.

The onion mascot, with his visor and wink, was part of the package. Fraser chose to announce the new team in a press conference at Sharpstein Elementary School, where children were given rally towels to cheer. After the announcement, Fraser took questions and one student asked him what the onion was named.

"I'd thought of everything," he said, except, somehow, a name for the team mascot. "On a whim, I blurted out 'Sweet Lou' and everybody cheers."

The name earned him flak from one of the team's owners, Jeff Cirillo, a former Mariner whose conflicts with former manager Lou Piniella are well-documented. But the name stuck.

Because the Sweets rely on college baseball players, the roster changes year to year. That makes it hard to build a fan following based on star players, so Sweet Lou fills the gap.

"Sweet Lou has become a face that we can market year in and year out," he said.

Fraser said he hopes the team can help preserve the onion's place in Walla Walla history, even as the wine industry grows in prominence.

"The first thing people came to know Walla Walla for was the onion," he said. "We don't want to lose that."

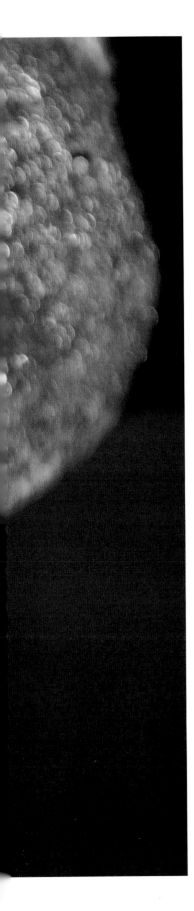

OYSTERS

Long before wheat or apples, tulips or potatoes took root on a commercial scale in Washington, oysters provided a lucrative economic export for the region's pre-state economy. Grown and honed through decades of innovative practices, the industry now faces a new threat, one which early harvesters could scarcely have predicted — ocean acidification resulting from global climate change.

STILL IN THE SHELL GAME

Oysters, among Washington's most lucrative, endangered crops

Story by Jim Camden, photos by Jesse Tinsley

THE SPOKESMAN-REVIEW

Washington farms don't stop at the water's edge.

The state's oldest "crop" — or maybe its first commercial "livestock" — grows in the bays, coves and inlets of the Pacific Ocean and Puget Sound, opening shells when the tide is in to pull nutrients out of the salty water and closing them tight against predators when the tide is out.

In 1851 — long before the Palouse hills were planted with wheat or the Okanogan Valley with apples — Washington oysters were harvested and shipped off to a waiting market in California, where Gold Rush miners were willing to pay top dollar for the tasty bivalves.

Washington oysters became so popular in the following decades that they were shipped around the country.

And they were so important to the early Washington economy that even before statehood, the territorial legislature allowed residents to own tidal lands where they could grow and harvest oysters and other shellfish. No state did that then, and no other state does it now.

That popularity almost became their undoing. The region's native oysters were so lucrative that by the start of the 20th century they were almost gone because of overharvesting, hard winters and pollution.

The introduction of hardier, faster-growing species in the early 1900s and continued improvements in growing techniques have brought Washington back to the top of the heap of American oyster production, and intense marketing is opening international markets. Technology provides a boost for most phases of a commercial oyster's life cycle, from a microscopic bit of fertilized plankton to its appearance on a plate of crushed ice in a restaurant.

OPPOSITE: An oyster boat moored at the Port of Peninsula unloads a mountain of harvested oysters, which are dredged from beds at high tide.

Oysters are a huge part of the state's shellfish industry, which ships internationally and relies on workers from around the globe to pump as much as $150 million a year into the state's economy.

Now the biggest problems facing the state's oyster crop are human-produced carbon pollution and the threat of global climate change.

Why, then the world's mine oyster, which I with sword will open.
— William Shakespeare, "The Merry Wives of Windsor"

With hundreds of small oyster-growing operations, some as small as a few acres, Washington produces more cultivated oysters than any other state in the country, said Julie Horowitz, senior policy adviser on ocean acidification to Gov. Jay Inslee.

But are they farmers?

"They call their babies seed and they plant them," Horowitz said. "They certainly see themselves as farmers."

The state's Department of Agriculture has an aquaculture specialist and shares some responsibilities with the Natural Resources and Ecology departments in improving the shellfish crops.

Just as there are differences in soil that require adjustments in techniques or crops for farmers on land, the shellfish industry is "constantly working at figuring out what grows well, where," she said.

Washington is trying to expand the area suitable for growing shellfish in the Puget Sound, where a century and a half of sewage from cities, runoff from farms and waste dumped from ships has wiped out many historic beds.

A coalition of state and federal agencies, tribes,

"You can plant 'em just about anywhere."

— Eric Hall

conservation groups and industry have combined to create the Washington Shellfish Initiative, to reduce pollution and restore some 10,000 acres of tidelands by the end of the decade. At last count, they had opened more than 2,400 acres but are behind the pace to meet their goal.

Just like their land-bound counterparts, oyster farmers are constantly adapting to pests, diseases and a changing environment. Burrowing shrimp can lessen the yields in Willapa Bay. Norovirus hit Hammersley Inlet, causing a recall of oysters from farms in that Mason County waterway.

But the biggest concern for oyster farmers throughout the region is ocean acidification from increased carbon dioxide in the atmosphere, which can be as quick as it is variable.

"During rush-hour traffic, we see changes in the water chemistry in Elliott Bay," Horowitz said.

He was a bold man that first ate an oyster.
— Jonathan Swift, "Polite Conversation"

Oysters, with various species growing around the world, have been eaten for centuries. They were a staple of coastal Native American diets, considered a delicacy in Asia and an aphrodisiac in ancient Rome.

When white settlers first arrived on the Pacific coast of Washington, they found great reefs of oysters in the water, which they began scooping up and shipping off. Miners during the California gold rush reportedly paid $1 apiece for oysters in San Francisco taverns. While that may seem a bargain compared to what you paid at a fancy oyster bar during that last trip to Seattle, with inflation, a dollar in the 1850s would be worth about $27 today.

OYSTER LIFE CYCLE
The graphic shows selected stages in the life cycle of the oyster.

Cell division
Fertilized oyster eggs undergo cell division until they become juvenile larvae.

Pediveliger larvae

Between 12-24 hours the larvae begin developing a shell and a foot to become veliger larvae.

After transforming into pediveliger larvae, with a well-developed foot and eye spots, the larvae are able to find a place to attach (usually an oyster shell) and become spat.

Spat
The spat will begin feeding and put all of their energy into shell growth. This is accomplished by isolating calcium carbonate from the water.

Mature oyster
At one year, the oyster becomes a juvenile and is an adult at three years.

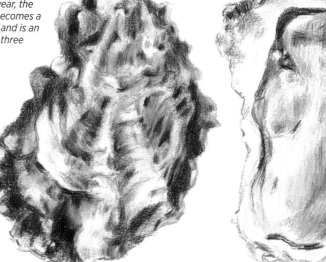

Sources: www.sarasota.wateratlas.usf.edu; hatchery.hpl.umces.edu; wdfw.wa.gov/fishing/shellfish/oysters

MOLLY QUINN/THE SPOKESMAN-REVIEW

Those native oysters were the relatively small Olympia oyster, Ostrea lurida. As demand grew for the small mollusk with a slightly sweet taste, Washington oyster farmers experienced a boom.

One problem with the Olympia oyster was its relatively slow growing process, as it takes about four years to get big enough to harvest. In a few decades, the beds that had grown up over the centuries were depleted, and Washington's oyster farmers began to go bust.

"By the 1900s, we were pretty much out of oysters," said Eric Hall, director of clam and oyster farming for the 7,000 acres of tidelands operated by Taylor Shellfish Farms in Willapa Bay.

The industry was saved by what today would be considered an invasive species. Desperate to replenish the beds, farmers tried to transplant an oyster from Europe, Ostrea edulis. It didn't thrive. In 1905, they brought a species from Japan, Crassostrea gigas, that did.

Known as the Pacific oyster in the United States, or the Japanese or Miyagi oyster elsewhere, it is relatively disease-resistant, hardier, meatier and faster-growing than the Olympia oyster. It quickly took over Washington's tidal lands and became the staple of the Northwest oyster industry. It's now grown on the shores of every continent except Antarctica.

"You can plant 'em just about anywhere," Hall said.

It is unseasonable and unwholesome in all months that have not an R in their name to eat an oyster.

— Samuel Butler, "Diet's Dry Dinner"

Most species of oysters, including those grown on the Washington tidal regions, are hermaphrodites, starting out their lives as males with some switching to females after a year or two. They typically spawn when the water temperature warms in summer months, which may be the basis for the long-held adage to avoid them between May and August.

Submerged, an oyster opens its shell and filters water and nutrients through its gills. When exposed to the air, it closes the shell for protection and can live for hours, even days, under proper conditions.

A female oyster can produce millions of microscopic eggs, fertilize them with sperm emitted from nearby males and eject them into the water.

Some 70 percent of all oysters in Washington are grown in Willapa Bay, a body of water on the state's southwest coast, fed by the tidal flows of the Pacific Ocean through a narrow opening between the Long Beach peninsula and Cape Shoalwater on the north and freshwater from mainland rivers on the east and south.

"We're the oyster capital of the world," Hall said as a small power scow — a flat-decked boat with a lift forward and steering cabin aft, designed and built by Taylor for tending the shellfish farms — zipped across the bay to one of the company's beds.

Some Washington tidal lands have been owned by the same families for generations, and some operations haven't changed much over that time, he said. When Hall was

OPPOSITE: An oyster bed belonging to Taylor Shellfish Company is at low tide, showing thousands of oysters, mostly in clusters, growing in the muddy tidal flats of Willapa Bay. The bay is the perfect place for growing oysters, which take about three years to grow into a salable product.

named director of Taylor's operations on the bay four years ago, he was determined to bring the best new techniques from around the world, rejecting any argument that "this is the way we've always done it."

On a sunny morning in October, Hall and one of his managers, Phil Stamp, were headed out to check the coupellas, an innovation imported from France.

Coupellas are 6-inch-diameter plastic discs with a hole in the center, arranged on rods that are stacked on a rack staked in the tidal lands. They are designed to be "landing zones" for fertilized oyster larvae.

Oysters start out their lives in a very vulnerable condition, near the bottom of the maritime food chain, microscopically small and shell-less. After being released by a female oyster in the wild, a fertilized egg can spend weeks moving through the water in a larval stage, until it secretes a substance that cements itself to something hard.

Larvae that reach that stage are called spats and begin pulling carbon and minerals from the water and surrounding environment to form shells. One of their favorite landing spots is the shell of another oyster. Because of that, oyster growers keep large mounds of shells after shucking to provide a starting point for spats. After a few weeks, a spat grows to the point that it's called a seed.

The old shells with the new seeds are often put in mesh bags that are staked in a tideland, where they grow to maturity.

The coupellas are a different technique. The racks of discs are staked on areas near spawning oysters so the larvae can latch on and begin to grow shells with some protection from predators. As the skiff pulled up to an area of racks at low tide, Hall and Stamp hopped off into the mud to inspect the coupellas they hadn't seen since the racks had been put out weeks earlier.

"It's un-fricking-believable," Stamp said as they

examined the discs covered with hundreds of light dots, spats that had adhered and were starting to grow.

In the coming weeks, the racks will be brought ashore to a nearby facility where the spats will get hosed off of the coupellas, grown in nutrients and eventually returned to the bay.

The advantage of the coupellas is that the process produces individual seeds that can be grown into single oysters. Growing multiple seeds on old shells often results in a cluster, which are suitable to be shucked for their meat that is sold in containers. But the greatest demand is for individual oysters, both in restaurants and at home.

Scrooge ... secret and self-contained and solitary as an oyster.

— Charles Dickens, "A Christmas Carol"

Although oysters are likely to grow in clusters, advances in technology are geared to growing them individually. Companies like Taylor have hatcheries where oysters spawn, and nurseries where the spats grow.

In nature, an oyster stays put once a spat has adhered itself to something hard. In 21st-century oyster farming, the process may move the young oyster thousands of miles over its lifetime. It might be spawned in a nursery in the Puget Sound and shipped to Hawaii to grow in water where the additional sunshine at certain times of the year grows more algae that provides food for the growing oysters.

It might then be transferred to California for a stint in warm waters and further growth, then back to Washington state to grow into a marketable seed. Eventually it can be placed in Northwest waters to reach a size where it can be harvested, graded and sold to an oyster bar in Seattle or New York, or flash-frozen and shipped to Beijing.

Everything an oyster needs to eat and grow it gets from the water filtered through the shell.

Once they reach a certain size, seeds are often placed in mesh bags staked on the tidelands. For large commercial operations like Taylor, those bags are arranged in rows and suspended above the flats so the ebbing and flowing tides lift and rock the bags, moving the seeds and keeping them separate as they grow. It also puts less of the oyster's energy into growing a shell and more into growing meat.

Through experiments with the bag placements, the growth period from seed to harvestable oyster can be cut from three years to nine months and can create a nicely rounded bottom shell much desired for the restaurant market. Oysters growing on tidal flats are dredged up by boats when the tide is in and dumped onto decks, carried to shore and shoveled into bins to be trucked to a processing facility. Those growing in bags are harvested by cutting the bag from its frame and bringing it to shore, where the single oysters get their first sort for size and quality.

"The more we innovate, the more people we need," Hall said. "That's our biggest challenge — labor."

Taylor employs about 50 people at its Willapa Bay farms, from longtime residents like manager Stamp, born and raised on the Long Beach peninsula in sight of the water where he works, to immigrants like Roberto Quintana, an expert in genetics and aquaculture from Mexico who operates the Bay Center nursery where larvae grow in large vats of water. Special strains of algae are grown for feed, and the pH and oxygen levels are controlled to mimic the bay where young seeds will be sent for further growth.

"At the end of the day, it's farming," said Quintana, who as a youth grew up around farms and idolized Jacques Cousteau.

When God made the oyster, he guaranteed his absolute economic and social security. He built the oyster a house, his shell, to shelter and protect him from his enemies.

— Author unknown, from the poem "The Oyster And The Eagle" used in the Eagle Scout ceremony.

In an oyster nursery floating on Oakland Bay northwest of Shelton, Washington, Bill Dewey walked between rows of bins with seeds of various sizes resting on the bottom of each container. A paddle wheel pumped water from the bay through the rows of containers, allowing individual seeds to feed on the nutrients in the bay water while they grow to a size where they can be sent to Taylor plots around the Northwest or sold to other growers.

"The South Sound is one of the best areas in the world for growing shellfish," Dewey, senior director of public affairs for Taylor, said as he pulled a seed, which looked like a fully formed oyster the size of a thumbnail, from a 3-by-3-foot container.

Along with Pacific oysters, other varieties like Kumamoto, Shigoku and Virginica are grown in the various bays, coves and canals of the Sound, and even some of the original Olympia oysters grow not far from the capital. Then there are the clams, Manila and geoduck, and mussels.

Different varieties of oysters planted in different areas develop distinct flavors from that location. In the growing restaurant market, discriminating oyster lovers can appreciate the differences, much the way an oenophile can seek out a particular vintage from a particular vineyard.

But the Northwest is also at the point of the spear for environmental and ecological challenges the shellfish industry faces. Along with the man-made problems that flow from the land, oysters face even bigger dangers from the air and the sea itself.

Higher levels of carbon dioxide are making the eastern Pacific and the Puget Sound more acidic, and that's very bad for oysters. To understand why requires a bit of chemistry knowledge:

When carbon dioxide in the air mixes with the salt water of the ocean, it produces a series of chemical reactions. More carbon dioxide in the air means more hydrogen ions and fewer carbonate ions in the water, changing the ocean's pH level to be slightly less alkaline, or more acidic.

The amount of carbon dioxide in the atmosphere varies naturally, so marine animals have evolved to tolerate some level of pH change.

The buildup of atmospheric carbon dioxide in recent decades — mainly from burning fossil fuels and overcutting forests that pull carbon dioxide from the air and store it — is reducing the carbonate that oyster larvae and other shellfish need to build their shells. When the carbonate level gets low, it's hard for young shellfish to grow shells;

> "The more we innovate, the more people we need. That's our biggest challenge — labor."
>
> — Eric Hall

when it gets really low, shells that have already grown can dissolve.

"The global increase in atmospheric carbon dioxide from human activity is large enough to reduce seawater (mineral concentrations) by biologically significant amounts," researchers Jan Newton and Terrie Klinge, University of Washington, said in the study "Ocean Acidification in the Pacific Northwest."

Northwest waters are also colder than much of the ocean, and less salty because of all the freshwater that flows in from the Cascades and Olympics. The water in the ocean is not the same from top to bottom, and the deeper water farther from the shore is often full of corrosive substances. When it gets pushed toward the surface areas, a process called upwelling, that also can affect the shellfish.

Upwelling can be cyclical. In 2008-09, it may have changed the carbonate levels at the Taylor nursery in Hood Canal and caused a 75 percent drop in the larvae production, creating a "seed crisis," Dewey said. Now the nurseries monitor carbonate regularly and can add chemicals to boost levels if they get low.

But carbon dioxide in the atmosphere continues to rise at a rate that some projections say could reduce the carbonate concentration in Northwest waters by 50 percent by the end of the 21st century. "That's a big deal if you're a shellfish," he said.

Oysters are so vital to the state economy that Washington has joined an international alliance with Norway, Chile, Portugal, Indonesia and Fiji to fight ocean acidification, with Gov. Jay Inslee focusing attention on the problem, Dewey said.

"O Oysters," said the Carpenter / "You've had a pleasant run! / Shall we be trotting home again?" / But answer came there none — / And this was scarcely odd, because / They'd eaten every one.

— Lewis Carroll, "Through the Looking Glass"

Twenty-five years ago, about 80 percent of Washington's oyster crop was shucked, preserved and sold in containers, used for stew, stuffing or frying. About 20 percent was sold to be opened individually and eaten on the half shell in restaurants, bars and homes.

"Now that's reversed," Dewey said.

Demand is so great that the supply of fresh oysters continues, even in months without an "R." Through cross-breeding, aquaculturists have developed an oyster that does not spawn in the summertime.

Taylor and other companies in Washington still process and can oysters on a massive scale, with lines of shuckers popping open the shells and depositing the meat in containers.

In a room chilled to 45 degrees, more than a dozen shuckers grabbed oysters from a conveyor belt and with a quick jab and deft strokes separated meat from shell, dropping the former in a container. When their containers

get full, they take them to a counter to be washed and graded by size before processing and packaging. The biggest ones go to the Asian countries, or Asian stores in the United States.

All the oysters on the conveyor are from the same farm, in order to track from harvest to table everything that's sold. When a new shipment from a different farm is delivered, shuckers take a break and the belt is cleaned to avoid mixing batches from different plots.

Shuckers start out at minimum wage, but those who last quickly move to piecework, getting paid by the gallon. A good shucker can deliver as many as 50 gallons a day; it takes about 120 oysters to make a gallon. (For those who struggle with math, that's roughly 6,000 oysters.)

The shucking crew is an international mix — Hispanic, Vietnamese and Cambodian, along with Caucasians, both American-born and immigrants. Hooded and layered against the cold, the racial and ethnic differences are almost indistinguishable until the shucking stops and they walk away from the belt.

In another processing plant down the road, shuckers are opening individual oysters but keeping them in the half shell with their liquid for shipping overseas. This is a trickier process because an opened oyster doesn't stay fresh and edible long.

These are the top-quality Shigoku and Pacific oysters much in demand nationally and internationally. They are flash-frozen with liquid nitrogen at minus 80 degrees Fahrenheit, packed in trays with molded indentations to hold the shells, then boxed and moved to a freezer until they can be shipped in refrigerated containers. They'll last three to six months, depending on the quality of a restaurant's freezer, and when thawed and placed on a plate, they will be close to fresh.

Cartons of the flash-frozen oysters awaiting shipment have labels marking them for delivery to New York, Boston, Hong Kong and Taiwan.

Farming the oceans and bays presents great opportunities, but also faces great challenges for government, science and the industry to overcome, Dewey said.

If that can happen, "there's an opportunity to feed the world's population with aquaculture," he said.

OPPOSITE: Workers joke around on the busy shucking line at the Taylor Shellfish Company processing plant in Shelton, Wash. Many workers in the processing plants are Hispanic.

ABOVE: Eric Hall, Director of Clam and Oyster Farming at the Willapa Bay operation of Taylor Shellfish, inspects a "flip bag," a hard plastic mesh bag in which his company raises oysters on the Long Beach tidal flats. The bags produce excellent single oysters, which are prized for serving in oyster bars and fetch top dollar on the seafood market, as opposed to those grown in clusters.

Open 2 dozen oysters in under 2 minutes?
Shucks, yes

Story by Jim Camden, photos by Tyler Tjomsland
THE SPOKESMAN-REVIEW

SHELTON, Wash. — Just as ranching has rodeo and farming has tractor pulls to show off certain work skills, shellfish farming has oyster shucking contests, ranging from local to national to international.

The timed opening of oysters features audience participation unlike any other competition.

The West Coast Oyster Shucking Championships take place every fall during Oysterfest, a two-day state seafood festival just outside Shelton where community groups raise money for the coming year's activities at booths that sell everything from scallops wrapped in bacon to smoked salmon and fry bread. And, of course, oysters cooked about every imaginable way, from barbecued to fried to Rockefeller-ed.

On the first day, shuckers vie to be the fastest to open two dozen oysters and plop the meat on a plate as quickly as possible, as on the processing line. On the second day, they again open two dozen oysters but are judged on speed and presentation for arranging them neatly in the half shell, as though presenting them to customers at a restaurant.

The skills are not completely interchangeable. Production line shuckers usually open an oyster by inserting a knife at the "bill" where the shell separates to open in the water. Restaurant shuckers usually open it from the other end, where the shell is hinged together. The former is faster; the latter is neater and retains more of the oyster's liquid.

The winner of the speed competition wins $400; the winner of the half-shell competition, $600.

The knives are sharp. "We have had injuries in the past," announcer Mike Barnard said. "It makes the competition more exciting."

Shuckers who come from all over the West Coast compete in heats, with a judge standing behind each one. The nine fastest times from the qualifying heats compete for the championship.

As with any true sporting event, fans take sides and the contestants trash-talk, particularly the shuckers from Taylor and Jolly Roger Seafoods, one of the state's other major growers and processors, with disparaging remarks about who grows the better bivalves. Contestants pick 25 oysters from baskets and arrange them on the table in front of them. At the signal, the stabbing, prying and scraping start.

In two days, the shuckers will go through some 550 dozen oysters. Taylor, which sponsors the competition, supplies the oysters and matches prize money if its shuckers win.

In the speed competition, some contestants struggle to get two dozen oysters open in five minutes. Others are done in under two. Juan Loza, a Taylor employee from Shelton, breezed through the second heat in about 1 minute, 45 seconds, and actually opened 26 oysters. The meat of two

of his original oysters plopped out of the shell and onto the ground. They couldn't be counted, so he grabbed and opened two more.

Loza said he came to the state from Jalisco, Mexico, in 1988 at age 16, and after spending time picking apples and cherries in Eastern Washington he came west. He's worked at Taylor for 20 years, seven of them as a shucker. His rule for picking a competition oyster: Get a flat one.

Each heat is followed by a waste-not, want-not tradition. Audience members crowd around the shucking tables to eat the oysters that have been flicked onto the plates by the shuckers.

In the final heat, Loza finished sixth in the speed-shucking competition, 16 seconds behind the reigning champion, Miriel Silva of Jolly Roger, who won the speed competition in 1:20:00. Silva would win the half-shell competition on a combination of speed and presentation, the next day as well.

The Oysterfest shucking champion used to be sent to the national competition in Maryland, which sends its winners to the international competition in Ireland. But not anymore.

"We were sending Cambodian, Vietnamese and Hispanic shuckers," Barnard said. "They didn't like us competing against their white guys."

ABOVE: Eric Hall, manager of shellfish farming at Willapa Bay for Taylor Shellfish Farms, opens and inspects a fresh Shigoku oyster. Shigoku, Japanese for "ultimate," is the name given to oysters grown in mesh bags that are consistent in size and quality.

OPPOSITE: Misael Quirino, one of the fastest oyster shuckers at Taylor Shellfish Company, fills racks with half-shell oysters. The oysters will be frozen with liquid nitrogen and shipped overseas.

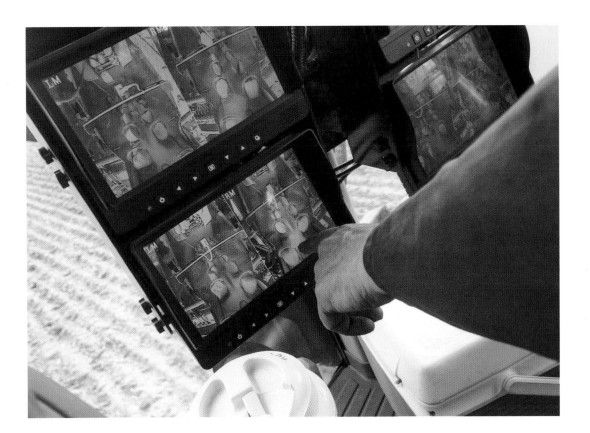

LEFT: Albert Wollman points to an elaborate camera system allowing him to monitor every seed potato that comes out of his planter at the Warden Hutterite Colony in Warden, Wash.

OPPOSITE: Rex Calloway shows the sizes of potatoes waiting to be cut into seeds during a tour in Quincy, Wash. Getting the spuds cut into uniform shapes and sizes is essential to planting efficiency and crop yield.

POTATOES

The potato farmer is the underappreciated backbone of the American diet. This in-depth look at the Washington potato addresses the importance of the crop to the economy, the future of the mighty spud, and offers a glimpse of the lives of two very different potato farmers.

'A HUGE LEAP OF FAITH'

Low profit margins, competitive market make potatoes a high-stakes investment

Story by Eli Francovich, photos by Tyler Tjomsland
THE SPOKESMAN-REVIEW

Rex Calloway looked west through the large windows of his 1950s-era farmhouse near Quincy and talked about the time, nearly 70 years ago, that his grandfather first arrived on this land.

Back then, the Columbia Basin was dry. A rugged landscape of sagebrush and rolling hills. Rattlesnakes. Scorching summer days. Cold nights. Quincy, the nearest town, was a speck, homesteaders and dry-land farmers eking out an existence on an average of 6 to 8 inches of rain a year.

"A huge leap of faith," Calloway called his grandfather's decision to move from Oklahoma.

But things were changing and Calloway's grandfather, who was 60 years old at the time, knew it.

"Water was coming," Calloway said.

Roughly 100 miles to the northeast, the Grand Coulee Dam was rising. And with it, a massive federal irrigation project that would transform the basin into one of the nation's richest farming areas.

Now, 70 years later, the Columbia Basin is one of the premier potato-growing regions in the country. While Idaho produces more potatoes, Washington farmers claim efficiency, harvesting about 60,000 pounds of potatoes per acre.

Most of Calloway's 2,700-acre farm is dedicated to potatoes. When he's not growing potatoes he plants corn and wheat.

On a recent Friday morning, he is busy. It's the first day of planting season, and he's about two weeks behind schedule

---

OPPOSITE: Albert Wollman stops his potato planter to manually check on the spacing between seeds while planting at the Warden Hutterite Colony in Warden, Wash. The spacing of each seed is key to maximum crop yield.

because of the unusually heavy spring rains.

"It's thrown a pretty big one (curveball) at us this spring," he said of the rain.

Calloway is just one piece of a statewide industry with a worldwide reach.

As big as that industry is, it's not an easy way to make a living. Shrinking profit margins in an increasingly competitive international market make potatoes a high-stakes investment with plenty of risk and little room for error.

And with that competition and specialization comes new demands. Farmers are increasingly expected to be business managers, chemists, mechanics and salesmen, in addition to farmers — belying the romantic, pastoral image many nonfarmers may have of agriculture.

"Farming is difficult. This is not easy. This is not easy," said Calloway, a third-generation farmer. "By God, if your heart is not in this, it will take you down so fast."

A massive state industry

In an unassuming Moses Lake office, Chris Voigt and Ryan Holterhoff oversee the Washington State Potato Commission. Baskets of sample potatoes sit in the entryway. Washington state potato souvenirs line the walls.

Voigt is the executive director of the potato commission,

"These are my spuds. I'm not working for somebody else. It's not my job. It's my responsibility to make sure these get planted right."

— *Nick Wollman*

which helps fund potato-related research, works to develop export markets and advocates for farmers at the state and national levels.

Potatoes are worth $7.4 billion to the state's economy each year, Voigt said. Although there are only 250 potato growers, the crop creates 36,000 jobs throughout Washington.

Those numbers contribute to the potato's status as the leading vegetable crop in the United States, representing about 15 percent of all farm vegetables sold, according to the United States Department of Agriculture. Washington accounts for 23 percent of the national industry.

The first domesticated potatoes were grown in present-day Peru and Bolivia between 5000 and 8000 B.C.

In fact, according to one 1990s economics study by Nathan Nunn and Nancy Qian of Harvard University, the cultivation of potatoes accounted for roughly one-quarter of the growth in the Old World between 1700 and 1900.

In 1995, a potato became the first vegetable grown in space. When humans go to Mars, potatoes may very well come along too. In 2015, potatoes played a prominent role in the Matt Damon movie "The Martian."

Washington potatoes are an integral part of this worldwide industry. Yet the scope of Washington's potato

WASHINGTON POTATO PRIMER

FINGERLING

Small, finger-shaped potatoes with a texture much like reds. Their unusual shape and size make them popular for plate presentations.

PURPLE/BLUE

Have a moist, firm flesh and nutty, earthy flavor. The best way to preserve the color is microwaving, but steaming and baking are also delicious.

RED

Have low to medium starch and high to medium moisture and are often described as waxy and hold their shape when cooked.

WHITE

Have a thin skin, so they can be easily mashed without peeling. Their creamy texture and mild flavor make them perfect for grilling and boiling.

YELLOW/GOLD

Slightly sweet, with a smooth, slightly waxy texture. They can be boiled, mashed or roasted and add a buttery color and flavor to dishes.

RUSSETS

Because they are high in starch (solids) and low in moisture they are the very best for baking, mashing and french frying.

Source: Washington State Potato Commission

industry isn't known by the average consumer, said Holterhoff, director of marketing and industry affairs for the potato commission.

"We have this very important and vibrant potato industry going on here in Washington," he said. "And if you get outside of the Columbia Basin, a lot of people don't even know that exists."

That's largely because about 70 percent of the 10 billion pounds of potatoes grown annually in Washington are exported.

"Right now the country of Japan buys more potatoes from Washington than anywhere else in the world," Holterhoff said.

Blame the weather. Four typhoons hit Japan's richest agricultural region in August, decimating the country's own potato industry and causing a potato chip shortage.

American consumers also rarely see Washington potatoes on the supermarket shelves, because most are sold to processing plants in Washington, like Lamb Weston, Simplot and McCain Foods. These plants process the potatoes, turning them into french fries, potato flour, potato chips, frozen potato products or other goods.

And although nearly all Washington potato farms are family-owned and operated, they aren't stereotypical mom-and-pop operations. Instead, they're large, sophisticated, multimillion-dollar businesses that rely on cutting-edge science and technology. On average, potato farms cost about $5,000 per acre to run. That's on top of the cost of irrigated land, which can be between $12,000 and $15,000 per acre.

And that largely has to do with the increasing competitiveness and difficulty of modern farming.

"If you have a decent year, a good year, you might make 4 percent return on your investment," said Voigt, the executive director of the state commission. "If you have something bad happen, you're going to lose money."

The small margins, combined with the high-tech machinery necessary to grow potatoes on a large scale, make consolidation and expansion a necessity.

"The margins have gotten so slim," Voigt said. "To make a living for your family anymore, you have to grow bigger."

No cold starts

When Calloway's grandfather came to Washington,

he bought land and started farming. Now, that's nearly impossible, with little available land and the high start-up costs of modern agriculture.

Although sometimes an established farmer will hire or train a new farmer, starting from scratch is too expensive, and too risky. Unless, Calloway joked, you're Jeff Bezos.

"To start farming, just to come into it cold, it doesn't happen," Calloway said. "You do not get somebody cold-starting a farm."

The lack of new farmers underscores another underlying problem for potato farmers and agriculture in general.

As younger generations become increasingly disinterested in farming, family farms often are auctioned when elder farmers retire.

Calloway has two sons, a 15-year-old and a 12-year-old, and although they help around the farm in the summers, it's not a sure bet that they will take over the farm when he retires.

"Are my boys going to farm? I would love it for them to farm," Calloway said.

But his boys may choose not to. If that happens, Calloway might be forced to auction his farm.

The average age of the American farmer was 58 years old in 2012, according to the U.S. Agricultural Census. What's more, the number of new farmers — those operating for 10 years or less — dropped by 20 percent between 2007 and 2012.

"I've seen more auctions this year than I've ever seen," said Paul Wollman, the farm manager at the Warden Hutterian Brethren farm, east of Calloway's farm. "This, here, is getting to the point where it's a big concern."

More management, less dirt

"It's what we've been doing for many generations," said 21-year-old Nick Wollman while perched in the cockpit of a half-million-dollar potato planter.

He added, "These are my spuds. I'm not working for somebody else. It's not my job. It's my responsibility to make sure these get planted right."

Wollman watched four video screens showing recently cut seed potatoes being deposited into the rich earth of one of the Hutterite fields. The tractor is GPS-controlled, driving in nearly perfect half-mile lines. Wollman's job is that of machine overseer. He makes sure systems are running correctly, that the potatoes are evenly spaced and chemicals evenly applied. And then, when he reaches the end of a row, he turns the machine around, and lets the GPS take over again.

Wollman is one of the 126 people who live at the Warden Hutterite Colony near Warden, in Grant County.

Members of the Warden Hutterite Colony work on their mechanized seed-cutting system in Warden, Wash.

POTATO PRODUCING COUNTIES

Superior management practices help Washington's potato growers maximize the land. Ready access to deep-water ports in Seattle and Tacoma provide easy access to ship potatoes throughout the world.

Source: Washington State Potato Commission

WORLD MARKET FOR WASHINGTON POTATOES

About 70 percent of all potatoes grown in Washington state are marketed out of the state with a significant portion going overseas.

SOUTH KOREA $65 million

JAPAN $220 million

PHILIPPINES $55 million

CANADA $30 million

MEXICO $35 million

THE SPOKESMAN-REVIEW

The colony was founded in the early 1970s as an offshoot of a Spokane colony. They trace their religious and cultural roots to the 1500s and the Protestant Reformation.

Paul Wollman, Nick's uncle, insisted that despite the farm's sophistication, at its core, it's essentially a big family farm.

"We're a family farm, and we are uniquely different from the farmer down the road," Paul Wollman said.

But what really makes the Hutterite situation unique, at least as far as farming goes, is the communal ownership.

"I can't say this is mine," said Paul's older brother, Albert Wollman. "It's all ours."

Nick Wollman's attitude toward his job illustrates the communal buy-in at the Hutterite Colony. Unlike most potato farmers, and farmers in general, the Hutterites don't rely on seasonal labor. Instead, they work together to plant and harvest the potato crop.

Back at Rex Calloway's farm, in a dimly lit, steel-reinforced concrete hangar, he's addressing a crew of six Hispanic workers he's hired for the planting season.

Calloway, a tall, lean man, hunched slightly to be heard by the shorter men and women gathered around a stopped conveyor belt. Potatoes sat on the belt bed. Small upturned paring knives are attached to the sides of the metal bin.

"Does everyone understand English?" Calloway asked. One woman shook her head.

So one of Calloway's full-time employees began to translate.

"What I'm trying to stress to you is safety," Calloway said. "Your hands only stay on the top deck."

These kinds of administrative concerns occupy most of Calloway's days, making him in some respects more of a manager and less of a farmer.

"I haven't sat in a tractor in 15 years. I don't plant, I don't till," Calloway said.

Later, he clarifies that on a regular basis he doesn't sit on a tractor, instead overseeing the farm's operations.

Calloway misses that hands-on work. He misses having dirt on his hands. So does Albert Wollman, Paul's older brother.

"Used to be we spent them (winters) in the shop fixing stuff," he said. "Now you spend them getting your certifications."

American nostalgia

Those changes underscore a profound shift in how American farmers ply their trade. Although food packaging and the popular imagination still depict pastoral scenes

of quiet country work, the reality is different.

While planting on an April afternoon, Nick Wollman reflected on the changes brought about by technology.

"Farming is a lot easier. It is not easy, but it's a lot easier nowadays," he said.

As evidence of the increased ease of farming, Wollman pointed to the tractor he's driving, or, to be more precise, monitoring. The GPS-guided machine travels up and down the rows in perfectly straight lines, with little or no human input.

Wollman has never driven a tractor that was not GPS-steered. His father, Albert Wollman, remembers the mental drain of focusing on driving straight lines for 10 or 12 hours a day. To keep the rows straight over a half-mile line, farmers marked out rows with rolls of paper towels half-buried in the dirt every 150 feet.

With the GPS guidance, Albert Wollman gets to read, often spending the days buried in the Wall Street Journal or the Atlantic.

"You get an opportunity to sit and think and whatever, read a book," he said of the planting season.

While planting, Albert and Nick communicate via radio. At one point, Albert's tractor stopped and he jumped out and started digging into the soil. Then he got back in his

tractor and started to back up.

"My computer crashed so I'm going to have to replant this row," he told Nick over the radio.

The cultural underpinnings of Calloway's farm, and that of the Hutterites, is one based on an ideal: the resilience and reliance of farmers, perpetuated in American culture through generations.

However, these same operations increasingly depend on mechanized and specialized machinery. Machinery that comes at a cost.

"I don't get my hands dirty. I have guys who get their hands dirty," Calloway said. "I miss it. I'd rather sit on a tractor."

LEFT: Rex Calloway chats with workers during a safety meeting at his seed-cutting operation in Quincy, Wash.

POTATO PLANTING SCHEDULE

PLANTING
The crop begins with pieces of seed potatoes or smaller whole ones. Planting can start as early as March and continue throughout the spring, depending on the variety of potato and the location of each farm throughout the state.

IRRIGATION
Sophisticated watering systems deliver to each plant the precise amount of moisture it needs. Some farms use center pivot irrigation systems that accurately deliver the proper amount of water.

STORAGE
Some of the crop goes from the field to processing or to fresh markets. However a greater percentage are stored for months in warehouses with optimum temperatures, lighting, humidity and ventilation. This ensures the availability of high-quality, farm-fresh potatoes year round.

JANUARY	FEBRUARY	MARCH	APRIL	MAY	JUNE	JULY	AUGUST	SEPTEMBER	OCTOBER	NOVEMBER	DECEMBER

BULKING & BLOOMS
A long growing season allows the potatoes to "bulk up." Washington state's warm days and cool nights contribute to ideal conditions for helping potatoes grow.

HARVEST
Early season harvest begins for certain varieties of russet potatoes, reds, whites, yellows and other specialty types of potatoes in July. In August, later varieties are harvested and the majority of harvest will be completed during September and October.

Source: Washington State Potato Commission

THE SPOKESMAN-REVIEW

Threats to the potato

Story by Eli Francovich, photos by Tyler Tjomsland

THE SPOKESMAN-REVIEW

Low-carb diet

In the late 1990s and early 2000s, something unexpected happened to the potato industry. The Atkins diet caught fire and millions of American vowed to lose weight by, among other things, cutting carbohydrates out of their diets.

Those eating decisions — person by person — changed the image of the potato and affected an entire industry.

"That was the big rage, that really had dramatic effects for about a three- or four-year period," said Chris Voigt, the executive director of Washington's Potato Commission.

He wasn't working in Washington at that time, but Voigt said there was an industry-wide double-digit drop. Washington, to some extent, was insulated because 90 percent of the state's potatoes are sold to processing plants.

"We're starting to see a little bit of improvement on potatoes and carbs," Voigt said.

A balancing act

Roughly 70 percent of the 10 billion pounds of potatoes Washington farmers grow each year are exported. So, the antitrade rhetoric of the November general elections worried most Washington potato farmers.

After his election, President Donald Trump withdrew the U.S. from the Trans-Pacific Partnership negotiations, a decision the Washington State Potato Commission disagreed with. The main concern? U.S. potato competitors, like Canada, are in free trade agreements.

In place of broad free trade agreements, Chris Voigt, the executive director of the commission, said it's imperative

---

ABOVE RIGHT: Nick Wollman examines his father's potato planter at the Warden Hutterite Colony in Warden, Wash.

OPPOSITE: Albert Wollman and his son, Nick, chat about their potato planters at the Warden Hutterite Colony in Warden, Wash.

the U.S. create bilateral agreements with other nations. Voigt points to Japan, which is the biggest international buyer of Washington potatoes. And that has to happen quickly, he said.

"If we don't have a free trade agreement in place, Canada will," he said.

At the same time Washington potato farmers worry about how Trump's trade deals will affect their business, they're promised deregulation will have a positive impact.

"Virtually everything we do, there is some type of regulation involved," Voigt said.

He hopes the Trump administration will critically examine the regulations to see what regulations aren't "serving a useful purpose anymore."

Future problems

The two biggest challenges facing Washington potato farmers in the next decade are trade and global instability, Voigt said.

"Any time there is global instability it can really disrupt international trade," he said.

On a more positive note, Voigt said potato farmers are turning their attention to soil science.

"Soils are kind of the next unknown frontier for agriculture to take a look at," he said.

Better understanding of soils may allow farmers to produce higher yields while also maintaining soil health.

60 days of potatoes

Voigt said that after eating nothing but potatoes for two

months, he'd never felt better.

Voigt started the diet in 2010 to draw attention to federal proposals to bar or limit potatoes in some programs, arguing that potatoes are high in nutrients.

"The challenge was I couldn't really add stuff to it," he said.

His publicity stunt drew international attention. Voigt started getting "potatoes from all over the country." He tried eating them all different ways, including juicing purple potatoes (which he doesn't recommend) and making potato ice cream (also not great, he said).

So, mostly he ate mashed potatoes.

The day Voigt ended his diet, he underwent a physical. His weight dropped from 197 pounds to 176 pounds and his cholesterol level fell 67 points. At the time, Voigt said he and his doctor were both shocked.

PULSES

A movement is underway to elevate "pulses" — a class of legumes that includes lentils, chickpeas, dry peas and dry beans — in the American diet, and Eastern Washington and North Idaho stand to gain. Versatile, healthy, environmentally friendly and an effective source of non-meat protein, pulses are increasingly seen not just as a rotation crop, but as a marketable, potentially lucrative source of income for American farmers.

PULSES ON THE PALOUSE

Versatile, nutritious legumes continue their push into mainstream culinary consciousness

Story by Chad Sokol

THE SPOKESMAN-REVIEW

Kale already had a reputation as a "superfood" in late 2014, when Beyoncé appeared in a new music video flaunting a chic sweater with the name of the leafy green spelled out in large varsity letters.

But Tim McGreevy said the superstar's endorsement gave the bitter vegetable a serious public relations boost. As the chief executive of the USA Dry Pea & Lentil Council, a national marketing organization headquartered on the state line between Pullman and Moscow, McGreevy wants to replicate kale's success.

"We are trying to get Beyoncé to put a lentils shirt on, too. And my God, we're going to make some sales if she'll do it," McGreevy said. "We're reaching out. We'll even take Jay-Z, although we'd looove Beyoncé, I'm telling you."

This would be just one part of an aggressive campaign to inject more "pulses" — the class of legumes that includes lentils, chickpeas, dry peas and dry beans — into the American diet.

McGreevy and his colleagues say pulses are versatile, affordable, nutritious and even good for the environment because they require relatively little water and fertilizer

> "There's more money in pulse crops now than there was 20 years ago, for sure."
>
> — *Allen Druffel*

and restore nitrogen to soil. By taking advantage of plant-based food trends and partnering with major food manufacturers, those in the pulse industry are aiming to popularize new ways of consuming the crops.

Sometimes maligned as food for the poor, pulses can be used not only in hummus and split-pea soup, but also in breads, noodles, breakfast cereals and crunchy snacks. And they can be refined to create ingredients like pea protein isolate, which is increasingly found in milk and meat alternatives. Such products include the super-meatlike Beyond Burger, which has recently appeared on store shelves across the country.

"We are all about pulses and redefining this category of foods," said McGreevy, who also leads the American Pulse Association.

Increased pulse consumption would be a boon for farmers in Eastern Washington and North Idaho. In addition to wheat — the main moneymaker on the Palouse — the region has long been known for producing lentils. The National Lentil Festival, hosted in Pullman each August, features the world's biggest pot of lentil chili.

But the star of the moment is chickpeas, due in large part to the explosive popularity of hummus, the creamy Middle Eastern dip in which they are the main ingredient. As Americans have learned to love hummus, Whitman County has become the nation's leading chickpea

producer, providing some financial stability for growers hit hard by recent declines in wheat prices.

Chickpeas are also known as garbanzo beans or "garbs," in farmers' parlance. And for growers like Allen Druffel of Uniontown, they are no longer just a rotation crop planted to improve soil health.

"There's more money in pulse crops now than there was 20 years ago, for sure," said Druffel, chairman of the Washington Pulse Crops Commission. "Back then, it was all about agronomics. We had to do it for the soil. But now we're making money on them. ... Now they're a cash crop."

What are pulses?

Pulses include lentils, chickpeas and dry green and yellow peas. They also include dry beans, such as pinto, fava and kidney beans. They don't include peanuts, or peas or beans that are eaten fresh, such as soybeans. All pulses are legumes, but not all legumes are pulses.

For whatever reason, this use of the word "pulse" hasn't quite caught on in the United States, although it's common in many other parts of the world.

"People always ask: What is a pulse?" said McGreevy, whose organizations are working to bring the term into the mainstream.

The word is derived from the Greek "póltos" and the Latin "puls," meaning porridge or thick soup. McGreevy said the history of pulse crops exemplifies how agriculture built civilization.

"Think of Roman times, when they were conquering the world," he said. "They didn't do it hauling a bunch of animals around. They actually had rice and a pulse crop on their backs."

This makes sense given how much nutrition is packed into pulses. They are high in protein and fiber — helping people feel fuller, longer — as well as micronutrients including magnesium, potassium, iron and folate.

Pulses are also gluten-free, a plus for those who have sworn off wheat and barley products. And they are significantly cheaper than trendy "ancient grains" such as quinoa.

"We think of quinoa as really high-protein, and it is. But one serving of pulses is twice as high (in protein), so it's a really significant difference," said Becky Garrison, a dietitian and nutritionist who oversees domestic marketing for the Dry Pea & Lentil Council and the American Pulse Association.

Garrison said pulse-based foods could be key to combating obesity, diabetes and heart disease and providing better nutrition in impoverished areas. She encourages people to incorporate a "half-cup habit" into their diets — at least three half-cup servings of cooked pulses each week.

To help people meet that goal, the Dry Pea & Lentil Council has hired food bloggers and published cookbooks featuring recipes such as Moroccan lentil tagine, pea and pesto soup, and butterscotch lentil cookies.

McGreevy said pulses can be incorporated into just about anything and can be a staple of a "flexitarian" diet. That's for people who are trying to cut back on meat but aren't ready to declare themselves strictly vegan or vegetarian.

"Just add pulses to everything that you eat, whether it's chocolate chip cookies or pasta salads," McGreevy said.

Corporate backing

The amount of chickpeas planted in the United States has exploded from about 30,000 acres in 1995 to an estimated 650,000 acres this year, according to U.S. Department of Agriculture data. McGreevy attributed this massive increase largely to the success of one

WHAT ARE PULSES?

Derived from Latin *puls* for thick porridge of meal, pulses are the edible seeds of various leguminous plants. Pulses are high in fiber and protein and when planted add nitrogen back into the soil.

LEGUMES

Soybeans   **Peanuts**   **Fresh peas**   **Fresh beans**

PULSES

Hearty fiber, high protein and sustainable

Dry beans   **Dry peas**   **Chickpeas**   **Lentils**

Sources: USA Dry Pea & Lentil Council, USDA, dictionary.com   **MOLLY QUINN**/THE SPOKESMAN-REVIEW

company, Sabra Dipping Co., the nation's leading hummus manufacturer.

In the mid-1990s, hummus sales in the United States barely topped $5 million, and many Americans weren't even sure how to pronounce the name of the dip. In 2007, PepsiCo and an Israeli conglomerate called Strauss Group each bought a 50 percent stake in Sabra, which then launched an aggressive marketing campaign, sending trucks into neighborhoods in large cities to distribute free samples.

Now, domestic hummus sales are on track to top $1 billion, according to some estimates, and the dip is a must-have for Super Bowl parties and on-the-go lunches. A 2016 survey found about 1 in 4 American households keep a tub

of hummus in the fridge.

"They got some big-time advertising dollars behind that effort and really put hummus on the map," McGreevy said. "We've been promoting hummus forever — for a really long time — but at the end of the day, we have to have some major food manufacturers with major advertising dollars to really start ramping up consumption."

McGreevy said the Dry Pea & Lentil Council, the American Pulse Association and their neighbors to the north, Pulse Canada, drained their coffers for a concerted marketing campaign in 2016, which the United Nations had dubbed the International Year of Pulses. Industry representatives also have met at conferences across the country focused on innovative ways to mill, cook, puff, pop, extrude and tease out the various nutrients of pulses.

Now pulses can be found throughout grocery stores, often slipped into familiar products or transformed into entirely new ones. Examples include lentil pasta, pea milk, crackers and cereals spiked with pea protein, pea protein powders and shakes, vegan mayonnaise made with frothed chickpea water, Tostitos chips infused with black beans, and a Cheetos lookalike surreptitiously named Peatos. Chickpeas and lentils have even been introduced into some types of dog food.

Interestingly, the world's giant meat packing and processing companies have invested in startups touting plant-based meat alternatives, taking note of growing concerns about the health impacts of excess meat consumption and the environmental impacts of intensive livestock farming.

OPPOSITE: Lentils, like these Palouse-grown legumes from Joseph's Grainery in Colfax, Wash., are low in fat, high in fiber and packed with iron, magnesium, Vitamin B-6 and protein. One cup has about 230 calories.
ADRIANA JANOVICH / THE SPOKESMAN-REVIEW

Tyson Foods announced in December it had raised its stake in Beyond Meat, the maker of the Beyond Burger. Cargill, the world's second-largest beef producer, has teamed up with Puris, the largest North American producer of pea protein isolate. And Canada's Maple Leaf Foods recently acquired Field Roast, a Seattle company that makes vegetable- and grain-based meat and cheese products.

McGreevy sees these investments as a good thing for pulse growers and processors.

"Meat companies are seeing that the trends are heading more toward plant-based proteins," he said. "They're not trying to shut it down ... because they see that this is what the consumer wants."

Profitable, sustainable

In Eastern Washington and North Idaho, pulse crops don't compete with wheat in terms of volume. They're usually planted in fields that would otherwise lie fallow, where they pull nitrogen from their surroundings and return it to the soil in a form that's accessible for the next wheat crop.

"If you plant wheat year after year after year after year, the ground is going to get sick of wheat," said Pat Smith, the chairman of the Idaho Pea & Lentil Commission. "And so you need to rotate those crops. And pulse crops fit in really fantastic for that."

Allen Druffel represents the fifth generation to work his family's farmland near Uniontown. He raises wheat,

LEFT: Farmer Allen Druffel examines the soil and root systems in his chickpea field near Uniontown, Wash.
TYLER TJOMSLAND / THE SPOKESMAN-REVIEW

barley, oats, canola and alfalfa, among other crops. When it comes to pulses, he prefers to grow peas, which require very little water.

But this year Druffel hasn't planted any peas. Chickpeas are again the most profitable pulse on the Palouse.

"The garb market is hot right now, and it can take the supply that we're producing," he said.

Druffel is actually growing two varieties of chickpeas, or "garbs." The smaller, variously colored desi variety is used primarily in hummus, while the larger, light-beige kabuli variety is usually sold whole, either canned or dried.

"Large garbs are graded on their size so you get better visual appeal," Druffel said. "So we'll plant those in the best ground, and we'll put the smaller ones in the drier stuff."

This is also the first year Druffel has bothered to spread fertilizer on any of his chickpeas. One morning in early June, he ventured into a field and pointed out a stark line between the fertilized and unfertilized crop. The plants that received an extra dose of nitrogen were several inches taller — worth the investment, he said.

Then he retrieved a knife from his pickup truck and dug out a plant to examine its roots. He was pleased to find dozens of white nodules, indicating that a healthy bacterium had invaded the plant and was doing its part to put nitrogen back into the ground.

"We're as excited about what's going on below the ground as we are about what's above it," he said. "Soil health is constantly on my mind."

With wheat prices down because of a global surplus, Druffel's chickpeas are helping sustain not only his land but also his business.

"It's nice to have other crops to turn a profit on," he said.

> "We're as excited about what's going on below the ground as we are about what's above it. Soil health is constantly on my mind."
>
> — *Allen Druffel*

LEFT: Olia Samolovov lifts her 5-month-old nephew, Zek Solo, in a field of sunflowers along Highway 395 near Deer Park, Wash. The colorful field of sunflowers is a favorite of photographers and spectators.
COLIN MULVANY /
THE SPOKESMAN-REVIEW

OPPOSITE: Honey bees and a large bumblebee share a flower in a field planted by farmer Dennis Urbat, who lives north of Deer Park, Wash. Urbat has planted the giant yellow sunflowers in several fields and will sell the seeds to make birdseed and sunflower oil.
JESSE TINSLEY /
THE SPOKESMAN-REVIEW

SUNFLOWERS

Dennis Urbat's original intention for sunflowers was crop rotation. And that's still a reason for growing the giant yellow sunflowers that attract crowds with cameras. Sunflowers are not considered a cash crop and the number of acres dedicated to them in Washington is relatively small. But Urbat, who started with just 40 acres of sunflowers, planted 900 last year and has found a market for bird seed and sunflower oil. Now if he can just find a way to cash in on all those lookie-loos with cameras.

BURST OF BEAUTY

Photo opportunities aplenty in a colorful crop sold locally for birdseed, oil

Story by Jim Camden, photos by Jesse Tinsley

THE SPOKESMAN-REVIEW

If only he could figure out a way to monetize their photogenic nature, Dennis Urbat might be able to get paid twice for his sunflower crop.

Once in the fall after he harvests their seeds; and again in summer for their ability to draw people who want their picture taken amid a field of big-headed, bright yellow flowers bending east in unison to catch the rays of the morning sun.

Drive north on U.S. Highway 395 past Deer Park in mid- to-late summer, and you'll see people posing in front of the fields Urbat and some of his neighbors grow as part of their crop rotation.

Sunflowers aren't Washington's biggest cash crop. Far from it. The most recent state agriculture census lists only 4,556 acres of sunflowers growing in the entire state, with 665 acres in Spokane County. But those figures are a year old; Urbat himself has planted about 900 acres this year.

He started about six years ago with just 40 acres. He was looking for something to rotate with his grain fields. He got the idea for sunflowers when talking to people at Global Harvest, where he sells wheat, barley and oats. The Mead food supplier needed sunflower seeds for the bird food mixtures it sells, and had to import them from

the Dakotas, which is at the top of a swath of the Great Plains that is prime sunflower-growing territory.

Global Harvest, the country's largest manufacturer of wild birdseed, could take all he could grow and more. Casey Thompson, the company's director of supply and

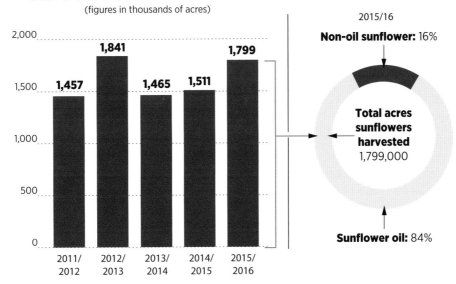

U.S. SUNFLOWER PRODUCTION
(figures in thousands of acres)

Source: sunflowernsa.com

MOLLY QUINN/THE SPOKESMAN-REVIEW

logistics, said the Mead facility is one of six the company has around the country and provides much of the wild birdseed that is sold at Costco, Walmart, Home Depot and most major retailers around the Northwest.

"Sunflower seeds happen to be the favorite food of wild birds," Thompson said. The Mead facility uses 10 to 12

million pounds of seeds a year.

In 2012, Global Harvest was looking to spread its risks for supplies by expanding production of different seeds to different regions. Urbat's decision to grow sunflowers benefits both local farmers and the company, Thompson said. They get a new dryland cash crop that helps rebuild their soil by pulling nutrients deep in the soil closer to the surface. Sunflower roots push deep into the soil and get the nutrients grains won't go after.

Global Harvest cuts down on its transportation costs and the carbon footprint of shipping seeds in from the Dakotas.

Urbat talked to a friend from North Dakota who used to grow sunflowers, wondering whether they'd do well in Eastern Washington. No reason why they wouldn't, they decided.

That year the U.S. Department of Agriculture listed 15 sunflower farmers in all of Washington, with 11 growing the plants for oil and four for seed.

He harvested the first 40 acres, sold the seeds to Global Harvest and planted 100 acres the next year. Then 250 acres the year after that. Each year, the acreage has grown and some of his neighbors now plant and harvest sunflowers, too.

He estimates there are now about 2,500 acres of sunflowers growing in Spokane, Lincoln, Adams and Stevens counties. The price for the seed fluctuates, but generally tracks with soybean prices.

They plant a variety of sunflower usually grown for

oil, but there's no facility to press the seeds locally and Global Harvest can take all being grown in the area for bird food.

Lisa Urbat, Dennis' wife, said the sunflowers fit in with their dryland family farm ethic, where they have a wide variety of crops, stress local sales and cut out the middleman through their collaborative effort with Global Harvest. They also bag up some sunflowers to sell on their own.

What makes sunflower seeds great for Global Harvest's feed mixes is a problem when the seeds are ready to harvest. Birds can pick a field clean almost overnight. The variety Urbat grows has a head that droops straight down when the seeds are ripe, making it hard for birds to sit on the stalk and eat the seeds.

Deer are another problem for a sunflower farmer. They enjoy munching on the plants.

One other pest is a danger to sunflower crops: people.

While the Urbats are happy to share the scenic nature of their sunflower fields with people who want a great backdrop for selfies, they struggle to keep people from entering the fields, trampling the stalks or picking the flowers.

Deer and birds are just doing what they do naturally, he said. "People should know better."

One year Urbat came upon three teenage girls in the middle of a field with armloads of sunflowers they had picked. They said they just thought the flowers grew naturally there. When he said they were his crop, they offered to put the flowers back. That won't work, he said, asking how they planned to reimburse him.

When they said they didn't have any cash, Urbat said he'd follow them to an ATM in Deer Park, where they withdrew some money. He charged them $20, which didn't really cover his losses but at least made a point.

Some people have suggested he try to get some money from all the photography, but he doesn't know a way to do that. Many of the fields are along the highway or next to country roads, and he can't monitor every section.

Sunflowers are harvested for the seeds long after the bright yellow flowers have wilted and turned brown. It requires some adjustments to the combine Urbat uses for his grains. The first few years he made some modifications in his shop to the combine's header to accommodate the plants that grow 3 to 5 feet high, getting some help from a friend and other information off the internet. Later, he bought a kit from a South Dakota company designed to handle the operation that collects the seeds and throws the rest of the flower out the back.

"It's just a matter of settings," he said. "You have to slow everything down."

RIGHT: Farmer Dennis Urbat, with his Jack Russell terrier, Remy, stands in one of his many sunflower fields north of Deer Park. The fields attract many visitors who mostly just take photos, but more than a few visitors will wander into the fields and damage the plants.

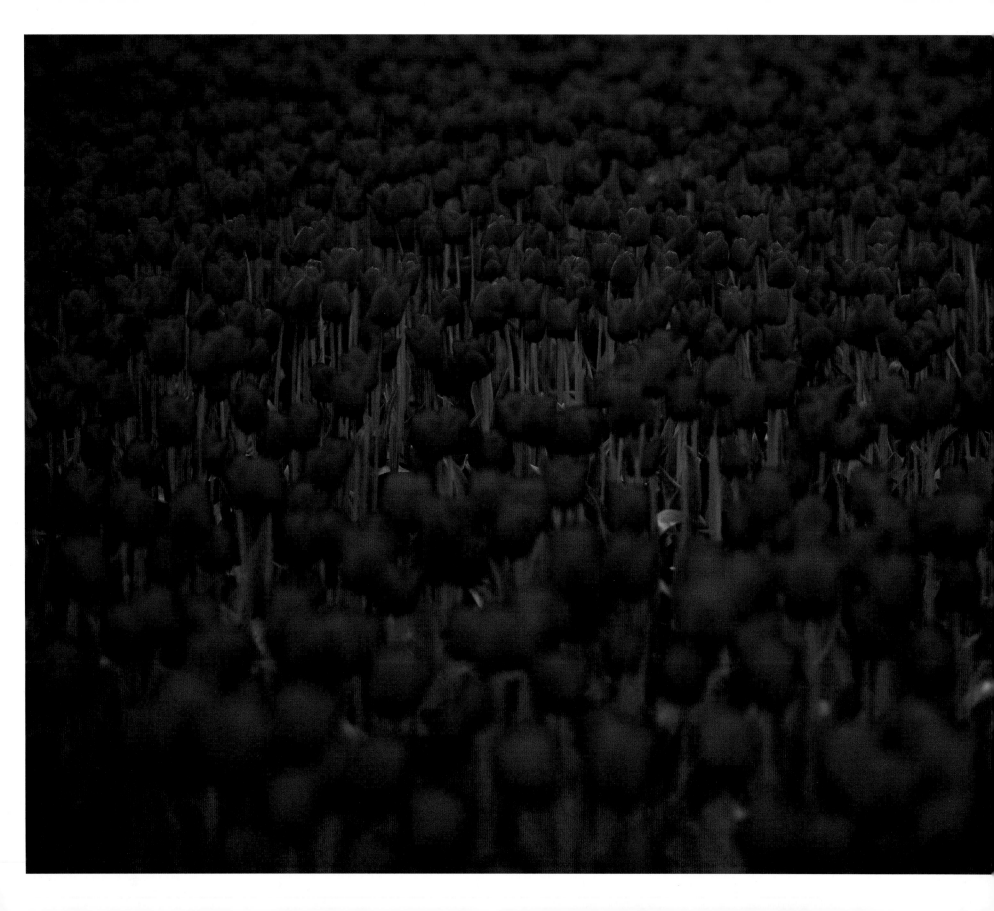

LEFT: Mike Flory and Bonnie Branch take a selfie amid a sea of color at Tulip Town near Mt. Vernon, Wash.
TYLER TJOMSLAND /
THE SPOKESMAN-REVIEW

OPPOSITE: The bright tulips create an amazing landscape at the Skagit Valley Bulb Farm near Mt. Vernon, Wash.
TYLER TJOMSLAND /
THE SPOKESMAN-REVIEW

TULIPS

The dazzling fields of the Skagit Valley provide the tulips that are a mainstay in flower gardens around the world. In the United States, nowhere are tulips grown in greater number than in the rich farmland bounded by cities north and south, ocean to the west and the jagged Cascade mountains to the east.

PEACE ON EARTH

Skagit Valley — at the heart of the U.S. tulip industry — draws visitors from around the world

Story by Eli Francovich, photos by Tyler Tjomsland

THE SPOKESMAN-REVIEW

Muriel Kenyon stood in a field of color that sparked memories of her mother and grandmother.

"It looks like this beautiful quilt that you could just curl up in," Kenyon said of the thousands of Skagit Valley tulips flashing brightly against the soft backdrop of a cloudy sky in April.

"It's pretty magical," she said.

Sixty miles south, Trinh Tran bought some of that magic with plans to fly it to Texas.

"I love tulips," she said. "In Houston, the weather is too hot."

After a brief negotiation, Tran struck a deal for dozens of tulips from a Pike Place Market seller in Seattle. She'll carry them on her late-afternoon flight back to Houston, injecting a jolt of Northwest color into her hot-weather home.

"I have never seen tulips this bright," Tran said, marveling at the bouquet in her hands. "Every single time I come here I get at least two dozen to take home."

Origins of a flower

Tran's desire to take those flowers home is not unusual. For hundreds of years, tulips have been packaged and transported around the world — a testament to our love for the colorful blossom.

First domesticated in the Ottoman Empire, tulips quickly became a status symbol in the Ottoman royal court. The word tulip is derived from the word turban — a nod

---

ABOVE RIGHT: April is the perfect time of the year for tulips just starting to open at Tulip Town near Mt. Vernon, Wash.

OPPOSITE: Workers top tulips as tourists mingle and snap photos at Tulip Town near Mt. Vernon, Wash.

---

toward the visual similarity between the two.

Tulips were first imported into Holland during the 16th century, and Dutch traders and aristocrats quickly turned the flower into an industry. A tulip craze swept Holland during the following century, creating what some economists call the first speculative bubble. Bulbs of certain varieties could cost more than a home.

Hundreds of years later, the tulip is still a sought-after commodity, filling Mother's Day bouquets, grocery stores and yards.

And while Holland remains the hub of the international tulip business, the Skagit Valley — a rich agricultural region of roughly a million acres between Seattle and Bellingham — is the heart of the tulip industry in the United States.

The valley's roughly 450 acres of tulips represent 75 percent of U.S. commercial production. About 300,000 people visit the fields during the monthlong annual tulip festival in April. Those tourists help put $65 million into the county's economy.

"We see double-digit increases in our sales tax from what is collected in March to what is collected in April," said Cindy Verge, the executive director of the Skagit Valley Tulip Festival.

For one month every year, tourists from all over the United States and the world descend upon the rural county. The attraction of the flowers may be obvious — bright, beautiful colors — but Verge said there is a deeper, more primal motivation at play.

"I think it's also a psychological thing," Verge said. "You get done with winter and it's like, 'Please. Let's have something bright and cheery.'"

The industry behind the bouquets

In 15 cavernous acres of greenhouse space, Washington Bulb Co. has made a business of packing and delivering "bright and cheery" tulips around the U.S.

In late April, tulips are prepared for the show of their lives.

"Mother's Day is just insane," said Brent Roozen, standing in the large greenhouse his family built.

In the lead-up to Mother's Day, workers make sure the tulips bloom at the same time and are collected into bouquets and packaged for shipping.

It's a complex undertaking. "If you have millions of flowers going out on Mother's Day, you don't want to be late," Roozen said.

Roozen works for Washington Bulb, the largest tulip

company in the United States. His grandfather, William Roozen, immigrated from Holland in 1947 and started growing tulips on five acres of land in the Skagit Valley.

Washington Bulb now owns roughly 2,000 acres of farmland in addition to its 15 acres of greenhouses. Of those 2,000 acres, about 350 are dedicated to tulips, with another 450 dedicated to daffodils at any given time.

The company has done well and still is owned by the Roozen family, being run by William's five sons. The company makes most of its money selling fresh-cut flowers. They grow tulips year-round in the greenhouses and ship fresh bouquets around the U.S.

Roozen said flowers cut one day can arrive in New York City at 9:30 the following morning.

After growing for a period in rectangular boxes, the greenhouse tulips are cut from their bulbs and shunted along a system of conveyor belts. They eventually are gently scooped up by mechanized claws and organized and arranged into bouquets, which are wrapped, boxed and loaded onto UPS trucks. Some head south on Interstate 5 to Sea-Tac Airport, while others head east across the state to Spokane. Washington Bulb supplies Spokane-area Rosauers with fresh tulips.

"What you order is what you get," Roozen said.

This side of the industry is not what most tourists see when they visit the tulip festival. Instead, they're treated to the acres and acres of outdoor tulip fields, which bloom in April.

Since 1968, fresh-cut prices have tripled while bulb prices have only doubled, according to Washington State University research. Since 2000, prices for both have decreased.

Fewer farms, fewer farmers

"Like any industry, there has been a lot of consolidation," said Don McMoran, the director of the Washington State University Skagit Valley extension. "The bigger farms tend to get bigger."

The trend toward consolidation in American farming is on full display in the Skagit Valley. In McMoran's lifetime, the number of bulb-producing farms has dropped from five to three. Of those three, only two produce tulips, and Washington Bulb Co. dominates that industry.

The other tulip operation, Tulip Town, has about 10

acres of farmland dedicated to tulips and focuses mostly on tourism.

McMoran said there are numerous reasons for the industry's consolidation. Increased global competition has forced operations to scale up in order to be competitive. For most consumers, place of origin doesn't matter that much when it comes to tulips. And larger industries based in Holland or South America take some of that market share.

"A lot of the product is coming (from) outside of the country to fill our needs," he said.

As in any agricultural pursuit, there are bad years, pests, infections and other unforeseen and unavoidable problems.

"The bigger you are, the more you're able to weather the bad storms," McMoran said.

Verge, the executive director of the tulip festival, said the loss of tulip growers in the valley worries her.

"It's very real that there are both economic and agricultural pressures," she said.

And despite the flowers' beauty, tulip growers are farmers at the end of the day — and farmers need to produce.

"Farming is a business," she said. "It's a tight business and the margins aren't real great."

Unlike most crops, however, tulip farmers get what Verge called "two harvests" — the April flower bloom and the bulbs. And the bloom, which attracts hundreds of thousands of tourists, brings its own rewards.

"There are very few places in the world where you can see something like this," Roozen said. "Especially so near to a metropolitan area like Seattle or Vancouver."

The peace flower

Jeannette DeGoede and her husband, Anthony, own Tulip Town. Relative to Washington Bulb Co., Tulip Town is a small operation, with just 10 acres of fields and no greenhouses. But DeGoede still thinks she has the best job in the world.

"I think it's one of the most wonderful professions because you see people happy," she said.

Instead of focusing on growing large acreage, the DeGoedes have doubled down on tourism.

A wraparound mural of Tom DeGoede's ancestral Dutch home greets visitors when they enter Tulip Town. A

garden, replete with windmill and pond, sits next to the farm fields. The DeGoedes bought their farm 37 years ago and just paid it off this year, Jeannette DeGoede said. For the past 25 years, they've been showing flowers as part of the tulip festival.

A centerpiece of Tulip Town's display is the International Peace Garden, one of many installed around the world.

The concept for peace gardens originated after World War II.

During the war, the Dutch royal family fled to Canada after Germany invaded Holland. When the war ended, they gifted 100,000 tulips to the Canadian Parliament. Now, the Canadian Tulip Festival in Ottawa is a yearly event and there are International Peace Gardens around the globe, including in the Skagit Valley.

Tulip Town's garden was dedicated in 2007.

"We really want them to be a symbol (of peace) on our farm," DeGoede said of tulips. "Because it's just what this world needs. People don't need any more wars."

A visual reminder

It has been nine years since Muriel Kenyon's grandmother, Virginia Kenyon, passed away. For the first time since her grandmother's death, Kenyon visited the Skagit Valley tulip bloom this April.

"It always makes me feel close to her," she said. "She was an incredibly smart woman."

Kenyon, who owns and runs a winery in Walla Walla, didn't come to the Skagit Valley with her mother this year. Instead, she texted her a picture of the flowers. Her mom responded, asking, "Did you run through them and try and take a nap like you did when you were a little kid?"

Kenyon restrained herself, she said. But the impulse to "curl up" in the fields of tulips was still there.

OPPOSITE: Rows and rows of tulips dominate the landscape at the Skagit Valley Bulb Farm near Mt. Vernon, Wash.

WHEAT

Wheat ranks among Washington's most valuable farm products, but the technologies that produce it — and the economics that bring it to market — are evolving. Farms that have raised grain for generations now look to a future of consolidation and change. And not only the farms themselves — Washington's academic institutions, which have long played a leading role in the development of new wheat strains, also face fresh competition from an expanding agribusiness sector.

GROWING GRAINS

Despite its importance, farmers say growing wheat isn't an easy living

Story by Chad Sokol, photos by Tyler Tjomsland

THE SPOKESMAN-REVIEW

The wheels of Bill Myers' black Jeep flung dust into the air at each bend of the gravel road that winds through his 3,300 acres of hilly farmland northwest of Colfax.

At the end of the road Myers passed a warehouse, where he stores equipment, and the 80-year-old home his grandfather built from a prefabricated Sears kit. Then he trudged through a field of dark northern spring wheat to a bluff overlooking the Snake River, where he swam as a child.

Much of the wheat was still green in early July, but an adjacent field had taken on a warm golden color. Myers, 66, wore a faded gray baseball cap and seemed unperturbed by the afternoon heat. His family has farmed for five generations, and he can't imagine doing anything else.

"Something gets printed on your DNA when you grow up someplace, and there's nothing you can do about it," he said.

Soon it will be harvest time, and Myers will truck most of his wheat to a nearby grain elevator, where it will be blended with wheat from neighboring farms. Much of it will be barged down the Snake and Columbia rivers, or hauled in trains to ports along the coast. From there it might depart to Japan or Egypt or Chile to become noodles or flatbreads or soft loaves called marraquetas.

Wheat is one of Washington's most valuable farm products, ranked among apples, milk, cattle and potatoes. Roughly 2.3 million acres in the state are put into wheat production each year. The industry employs thousands of Washingtonians and contributes hundreds of millions of dollars to the state's economy.

Yet farmers say it's no easy way to make a living. Because up to 90 percent of the state's wheat is exported, their

OPPOSITE: Bill Myers, standing in his wheat field that overlooks the Palouse River near Colfax, Wash., says he can't imagine doing anything else.

profits are at the mercy of a competitive global market. And to ensure a good crop, they must constantly protect their plants from diseases and pests — and hope for good weather.

"The farmers that are still around are all pretty good farmers," said James Moyer, the associate dean for research in Washington State University's agriculture college. "You have to be good to have survived this long, to have weathered all the storms."

'Feeding the world'

Hundreds of wheat varieties are cultivated in the United States, and each falls into one of six market classes, distinguished by their color, shape, hardness and time of planting.

They also vary by the regions in which they're grown. Soft white winter wheat accounts for about 80 percent of Washington's crop and is considered a specialty of the Pacific Northwest, while the top wheat-producing states — Kansas, North Dakota and Montana — grow primarily the hard red classes. Soft white varieties are ideal for Asian-style noodles and sponge cakes.

"People may think wheat is wheat is wheat, and might not have an appreciation for the different market classes," said Craig Morris, the director of the U.S. Department of Agriculture's Western Wheat Quality Lab in Pullman. "We have sedans and coupes and minivans and SUVs. We have

"You have to be good to have survived this long, to have weathered all the storms."

— *James Moyer*

all different shapes and sizes to market to people. It's very much the same thing with wheat."

Washington is known not for the quantity of the wheat it produces but for the quality, said Glen Squires, the chief executive officer of the Washington Grain Commission.

Because it's home to such varied climates and landscapes, the state is capable of producing a diverse wheat crop. Roughly 10 percent is hard red winter and roughly 10 percent is hard red spring. And under the soft white category there is a subclass called club wheat, named for its distinctive stubby head.

The specifications of each variety, such as protein content and gluten toughness, matter greatly to foreign buyers. The United States exports wheat to about 60 countries, with each buyer aiming to suit a regional palate. Some prefer wheat that can be refined into a starchy white flour; others want wheat that mills well as a whole grain.

"We routinely talk to the Japanese," one of the top consumers of U.S. white wheat, Morris said. "They have zero interest in whole grain wheat. They say, 'We eat lots of vegetables. We don't need it. We want white flour.'"

The United States produces about 8 percent of the world's wheat and exports about 46 percent of that, with much of it leaving through ports in Washington and Oregon.

SIX CLASSES OF U.S. WHEAT

Hundreds of wheat varieties are cultivated in the United States, and each falls into one of six market classes, distinguished by its color, shape, hardness and time of planting. They also vary by the regions in which they're grown and are used to make different products.

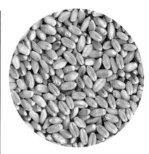

HARD RED WINTER	**HARD RED SPRING**	**SOFT RED WINTER**	**SOFT WHITE**	**DURUM**	**HARD WHITE**
The most common class of wheat grown in the United States, hard red winter is versatile and can be used to make pan bread, hard rolls, flatbreads and tortillas, as well as Asian-style noodles, cereal and general purpose flour.	U.S. Wheat Associates, an organization responsible for marketing American wheat to foreign buyers, calls this the "aristocrat" of American wheat, suitable for making croissants, bagels, pizza crusts, rolls and artisan breads.	With weak gluten strands, this versatile class creates dough with low elasticity, making it suitable for cookies, crackers, pretzels, pastries and flatbreads.	This class makes up about 80 percent of wheat grown in Washington. With little protein and weak gluten strands, it's ideal for Asian-style noodles, sponge cakes, pastries and cookies. A subclass of soft white is club wheat, named for its distinctive stubby head.	With a high protein content and strong gluten strands, durum is extremely hard and can't easily be milled into a fine flour. It is, however, perfect for making pasta and couscous, and is used in some Mediterranean breads.	The newest class of U.S. wheat, hard white can be used to make Asian-style noodles, tortillas and flatbreads, as well as whole grain flour that retains its white color.

Sources: U.S. Wheat Associates, U.S. Department of Agriculture

THE SPOKESMAN-REVIEW

Exports have fluctuated since the early 1960s, topping 48 million metric tons in 1982 and falling below 23 million metric tons in 2003, according to the USDA. In recent years, annual exports have mostly hovered below 30 million metric tons.

Although the country is still a major player in the global wheat market, it has in recent years fallen behind the European Union, Canada and Russia.

The USDA oversees two "market promotion" programs that help sell American crops in foreign countries. They support organizations like U.S. Wheat Associates, which has 15 international offices and works to maintain trade relationships and establish new ones.

In June, Casey Chumrau, who runs U.S. Wheat Associates' marketing operations in Santiago, Chile, led four Chilean businessmen on a tour of American wheat-producing regions. The group flew from Santiago to Oklahoma City to Sacramento to Spokane, then drove to several destinations on the Palouse, including the USDA lab in Pullman and a grain terminal along the Clearwater River in Lewiston.

The four businessmen represent milling companies in Chile's Central Valley and are collectively responsible for purchasing about 60 percent of the country's 850,000 metric tons of annual wheat imports, Chumrau said.

Chumrau's job is to take advantage of Chile's love for wheat by showing off what the United States has to offer. The average Chilean eats more than 200 pounds of bread each year, she said, placing it among the top per capita wheat consumers in the world. The United States and Canada alternate places as Chile's top foreign supplier.

"It's cliché to say that we're feeding the world, but, you know, it's actually true," Morris said.

A hub for wheat science

Archaeological evidence suggests wheat was domesticated as early as 10,000 years ago in the so-called Fertile Crescent region, in a spot that's now part of Turkey.

It was a primitive variety known as einkorn, which has 14 chromosomes. A 28-chromosome variety, called emmer, was cultivated later, and scientists believe it crossed with a weed, called jointed goatgrass, to create modern wheat's 42-chromosome structure.

Only in the past few years, however, have gene sequencing and related technologies begun to play a prominent role in wheat breeding, Morris said.

"Applied plant breeding really is an art, and most of it is done in the field," he said. "Now these genomic technologies are really starting to complement the traditional guy or gal who's out there in the field, looking at wheat and making selections."

Breeding is a laborious process that involves numerous rounds of experimentation. Morris said more than 99 percent of the breeds tested are never released, and it can

Bill Myers, giving a tour of one of his wheatfields near Colfax, Wash., says he is not considering retirement. At 66, Myers represents nearly a third of all U.S. famers who are 65 or older.

take a decade or longer to develop a variety that can compete in a crowded market.

"It not only has to be good enough for growers," he said, "It has to be better than what's out there already."

Morris' lab occupies a nondescript building on Washington State University's Pullman campus, a floor above Ferdinand's, the popular ice cream parlor and Cougar Gold cheese dispensary. There are other USDA wheat labs in Kansas, North Dakota and Ohio.

To assess the characteristics of each wheat variety that comes through the lab, Morris and his team of scientists

bake cookies. Lots of cookies.

Some turn out wide and flat with a slightly crisp, crackled surface. Others don't spread much in the oven, or there's something wrong with the flavor or texture. Each cookie is marked with a numbered sticker so the researchers know which kind of wheat it was made with.

The goal, Morris said, is to answer questions such as "What are the genes that make this dough strong but this one weak?" and "What are the genes that make this cake rise but this one flat?"

One of his breeding accomplishments is soft durum

wheat — a term that may sound like an oxymoron to many wheat farmers.

With a high protein content and tough gluten strands, ordinary durum is one of the hardest classes of wheat, ideal for making pasta and not much else. But when Morris and his collaborators bred durum with soft white wheat, they created something far more versatile.

Nearly 20 years in the making, soft durum is being grown commercially near Lewiston, and a pizza restaurant in Pullman uses it exclusively for its crusts, Morris said.

"It makes good pizza crust, it still makes excellent

spaghetti, and yet you can use it in cookies and scones and things," he said. "It opens up a whole new range of culinary uses."

A future for GMO wheat?

With the USDA and WSU breeding programs, Pullman has become a powerhouse in the world of crop science, said Moyer, the associate dean who also oversees the university's Agricultural Research Center.

Two years ago, WSU released its 100th wheat variety, named "Jasper" after the man who started the school's breeding program in 1894. It's a soft white winter variety developed specifically for the regions of Washington that receive 12 to 18 inches of rain annually.

"We have, if not the strongest, one of the strongest research programs anywhere in the world," Moyer said. "Our breeding programs are second to none."

Yet the industry has evolved over the past decade as corporations like Monsanto and Syngenta bolster their presence in the region, Morris said.

"When I started here in '89 it was essentially 100 percent university and USDA breeders," he said. "Essentially all the varieties were coming out of university programs."

The influx of private breeding and genetic engineering programs has created a sense of heightened competition, Morris said.

"The university breeders are still working hard, and still putting out varieties, and still being successful. But it certainly has changed the landscape," he said. "There's just more players in the game, and there's certainly more resources being spent on developing new wheat varieties and marketing those varieties."

Genetically modified organisms are created by copying genes from one plant or animal and inserting them into the DNA of another organism. Most GMO crops are corn and soybeans eaten by livestock or made into processed food ingredients such as cornstarch, soybean oil and high fructose corn syrup.

The seed conglomerates have been experimenting with GMO wheat in the Northwest in recent years, although no modified variety has been approved for consumption by the U.S. Food and Drug Administration, and some foreign buyers are wary of engineered food.

Kimberly Garland-Campbell, a winter wheat breeder who works in the USDA lab, said she doubts the corporations will find a market for GMO wheat that covers the cost of research and development.

"I'm a research scientist," she said. "If I thought GMO wheat were worth it, I'd be using it."

A changing industry

In 2012, when the USDA conducted its most recent agriculture census, the average Washington grain farmer was just shy of 57 years old. Two decades prior, in 1992, the average was younger than 52.

Farms also have become bigger and more commercialized. During that same period, the number of grain farms in the state declined nearly 57 percent, from 5,032 to 2,871, while total acreage remained almost flat.

The number of partnerships and individually owned farms dropped from 3,035 to 1,743, while the number of farms owned by family corporations grew 20 percent to 807.

Other types of corporations owned 25 Washington grain farms in 2012, up from 10 in 1992. The results of the 2017 agriculture census have not yet been released.

Farms are consolidating and farmers are getting older nationwide. Nearly a third of all U.S. farmers are 65 or older, like Bill Myers.

"Things have gotten awful centralized," he said. "It used to be everyone was involved in agriculture. It used to be a man could make a living on half a section, and then it was a section, and then it was 1,000 acres ..."

The world market determines how much grain companies will pay Myers for a bushel of wheat, and what specifications it should meet.

Last year, many farmers on the Palouse were hit by a plague of low "falling numbers" — a system that measures the presence of an enzyme that degrades starches. Wheat with falling numbers less than 300 is generally considered unsuitable for baking, as it produces breads and cakes that don't rise properly. And foreign buyers won't pay full price for unhealthy wheat.

> "We have ... one of the strongest research programs anywhere in the world. Our breeding programs are second to none."
>
> — *James Moyer*

"The system is not geared to our best interest as a grower," Myers said.

Low falling numbers are a product of bad weather, specifically high daytime temperatures followed by sharp drops at night. Morris, with the USDA lab, said it remains to be seen whether the problem will strike again this harvest season.

Due primarily to a global wheat surplus, the average price per bushel in Portland has tumbled from more than $8 in 2012 to less than $5 this year.

With the rising cost of equipment and maintenance, the average farmer in the state needs about $6 per bushel to break even, said Michelle Hennings, executive director of the Washington Association of Wheat Growers.

"We have no way of passing on that cost to the consumer as you would do with other commodities," she said.

The age of the farmers and the consolidation of farms go hand in hand, Hennings said. When younger generations look at their parents' farms and see little opportunity for profit, she said, "what's left for the farmer to do but sell?"

And, Hennings said, small wheat farmers and their families are increasingly embarking on other entrepreneurial ventures to balance their checkbooks.

"You don't see the farmer's wife staying home anymore," she said. "You see them working more to help supplement the income."

Around the time of the recession, Myers recruited his two daughters — one with degrees in agribusiness and marketing, the other with a degree in accounting — to launch a business selling the best of his crops across the Inland Northwest.

Through that business, called Joseph's Grainery, the family can get up to $60 for a bushel of wheat, more than 10 times what they would make by offloading it at the local elevator.

Myers doesn't know if his daughters will take over the family farm, but he doesn't plan to sell it anytime soon.

"I've looked at retirement from afar," he said. "I'm unimpressed."

WHEAT GROWTH STAGES *(Zadok scale)*

About 80 percent of Washington's total production is winter wheat. Winter wheat, planted in the fall, needs six to eight weeks of growth before the soil freezes. This is so the plant can develop a healthy root system before winter sets in.

WINTER

Plant acclimates to the cold; growth slows significantly

Vernalization (cooling of seed during germination to accelerate flowering) is required in winter wheat prior to spikelet differentiation.

SPRING

Leaf becomes visibly enlarged during the booting stage

Plant develops head within the sheath of the flag.

FALL

Winter wheat planted

There must be enough time before the onset of freezing temperatures for the plant to establish roots and develop tillers and a main stem.

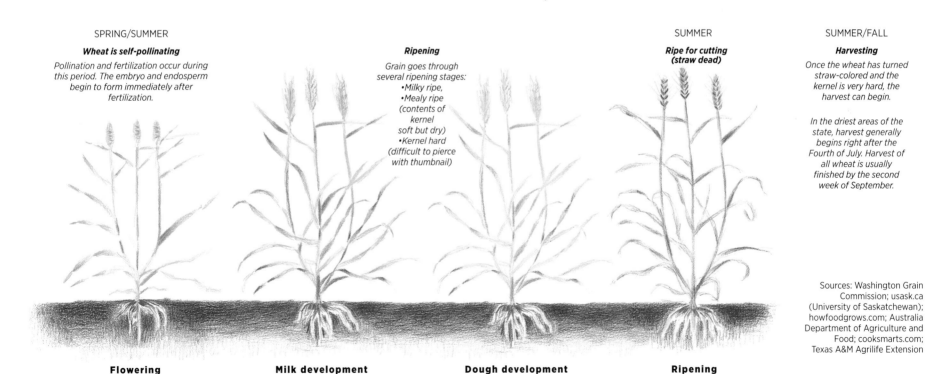

Germination

Seedling growth

Tillering (lateral branches)

Main stem elongation

Booting

Ear emergence

SPRING/SUMMER

Wheat is self-pollinating

Pollination and fertilization occur during this period. The embryo and endosperm begin to form immediately after fertilization.

Ripening

Grain goes through several ripening stages:
- *Milky ripe,*
- *Mealy ripe (contents of kernel soft but dry)*
- *Kernel hard (difficult to pierce with thumbnail)*

SUMMER

Ripe for cutting (straw dead)

SUMMER/FALL

Harvesting

Once the wheat has turned straw-colored and the kernel is very hard, the harvest can begin.

In the driest areas of the state, harvest generally begins right after the Fourth of July. Harvest of all wheat is usually finished by the second week of September.

Flowering

Milk development

Dough development

Ripening

Sources: Washington Grain Commission; usask.ca (University of Saskatchewan); howfoodgrows.com; Australia Department of Agriculture and Food; cooksmarts.com; Texas A&M Agrilife Extension

MOLLY QUINN/THE SPOKESMAN-REVIEW

WSU researchers show off varieties

Story by Chad Sokol, photos by Tyler Tjomsland
THE SPOKESMAN-REVIEW

LIND, Wash. — On a gray morning in the middle of June, more than 100 farmers, scientists and wheat industry leaders gathered at Washington State University's dryland Research Station, a cluster of fields and test facilities spanning more than 1,300 acres in Adams County.

The Lind Field Day is an annual exhibition of agricultural technologies and crop varieties being developed by WSU researchers. At one of the first stops on the tour, researchers showed off their latest iteration of a perennial wheat/wheatgrass hybrid.

Perennial wheat is something of a holy grail in the world of crop breeding, although it remains difficult to produce a sufficient yield, said Scott Yates, spokesman for the Washington Grain Commission.

"Just imagine if you didn't need to come in and replant your fields every year," he said.

Most of the wheat varieties presented during the tour were more traditional. Farmers received a firsthand look at varieties that may be available to them in the coming years.

There are stark differences between growing wheat in Lind, which receives fewer than 10 inches of rain in an average year, and in Pullman, which receives more than 20 inches.

"If you start at Colfax and you go east, the average annual rainfall drops by about an inch every 10 miles," said James Moyer, the associate dean for research in WSU's agriculture college.

It can be incredibly challenging to raise crops in the driest parts of Washington, as many farmers in Adams, Grant, Lincoln and Franklin counties rely on the shrinking Odessa Aquifer to irrigate their fields. As the quality and quantity of that water declines, potato farmers in the region are particularly susceptible and may be forced into dryland wheat farming.

Last year, however, was good to Ross Fox, who farms wheat on irrigated fields near Othello. While the weather caused unforeseen quality issues for many farmers on the Palouse, above-average rainfall gave Fox a high yield of good-quality wheat.

"We had our best crop ever in 115 years," he said, referring to the origins of his family's farm. "Moisture really makes a difference."

OPPOSITE: Local ranchers and farmers ride wheat trucks during WSU's Lind Field Day, an annual exhibition of agricultural technologies and crop varieties being developed by WSU researchers.

ABOVE: Gus Kiesz, a retired farmer, takes a closer look at some of WSU's experimental wheat during Lind Field Day.

CREDITS

THE PROJECT TEAM

Writers

Chad Sokol

Thomas Clouse

Rachel Alexander

Adriana Janovich

Jim Camden

Eli Francovich

Paul Turner

Photographers

Colin Mulvany

Jesse Tinsley

Tyler Tjomsland

Dan Pelle

Kathy Plonka

Editors

Rob Curley

Joe Palmquist

John Stucke

Jonathan Brunt

Nathanael Massey

Liz Kishimoto

Design

Chris Soprych

Michael Stephens

Molly Quinn